MW01092512

ASCE Manuals and Reports on Engineering Practice No. 45, revised edition

How to Work Effectively with Consulting Engineers: Getting the Best Project at the Right Price

Prepared by
The Task Committee for the Update of Manual 45
of the Committee of Practice Guidelines

Published by

ASCE American Society of Civil Engineers

1801 Alexander Bell Drive
Reston, Virginia 20191–4400

Abstract: This manual is intended to outline the functions of the consulting engineer in serving a client, explain the types of services usually offered, provide various methods of determining compensation for engineering services, and provide general ranges of remuneration received by competent consulting engineers for their services. A recommended procedure for interviewing and selecting a consulting engineer and guidance on contracts for engineering services are also provided. This work is designed to serve the best interests of both the client and the consulting engineer and to foster better understanding between them. The information offered is intended to apply to civil engineering practice, but certain aspects of this manual may not be applicable to specialty practice.

ISBN 0-7844-0637-5

Copyright 2003 by the American Society of Civil Engineers.
All Rights Reserved.
ISBN 0-7844-0637-5
Manufactured in the United States of America.
Library of Congress Cataloguing-in-Publication data on file.

MANUALS AND REPORTS
ON ENGINEERING PRACTICE

(As developed by the ASCE Technical Procedures Committee, July 1930, and revised March 1935, February 1962, and April 1982)

A manual or report in this series consists of an orderly presentation of facts on a particular subject, supplemented by an analysis of limitations and applications of these facts. It contains information useful to the average engineer in his everyday work, rather than the findings that may be useful only occasionally or rarely. It is not in any sense a "standard," however; nor is it so elementary or so conclusive as to provide a "rule of thumb" for nonengineers.

Furthermore, material in this series, in distinction from a paper (which expresses only one person's observations or opinions), is the work of a committee or group selected to assemble and express information on a specific topic. As often as practicable, the committee is under the direction of one or more of the Technical Divisions and Councils, and the product evolved has been subjected to review by the Executive Committees of these Divisions or Councils. As a step in the process of this review, proposed manuscripts are often brought before the members of the Technical Divisions and Councils for comment, which may serve as the basis for improvement. When published, each work lists the names of the committees by which it was compiled and clearly indicates the several processes through which it has passed in review, in order that its merit may be definitely understood.

In February 1962 (and revised in April 1982) the Board of Direction voted to establish:

A series entitled *Manuals and Reports on Engineering Practice*, to include the Manuals published and authorized to date, future Manuals of Professional Practice, and Reports on Engineering Practice. All such Manual or Report material of the Society would have been refereed in a manner approved by the Board Committee on Publications and would be bound, with applicable discussion, in books similar to past Manuals. Numbering would be consecutive and would be a continuation of present Manual numbers. In some cases of reports of joint committees, bypassing of Journal publications may be authorized.

MANUALS AND REPORTS
ON ENGINEERING PRACTICE

No.	Title	No.	Title
13	Filtering Materials for Sewage Treatment Plants	73	Quality in the Constructed Project: A Guide for Owners, Designers, and Constructors
14	Accommodation of Utility Plant Within the Rights-of-Way of Urban Streets and Highways	74	Guidelines for Electrical Transmission Line Structural Loading
35	A List of Translations of Foreign Literature on Hydraulics	76	Design of Municipal Wastewater Treatment Plants
40	Ground Water Management	77	Design and Construction of Urban Stormwater Management Systems
41	Plastic Design in Steel: A Guide and Commentary	78	Structural Fire Protection
45	Consulting Engineering: A Guide for the Engagement of Engineering Services	79	Steel Penstocks
46	Pipeline Route Selection for Rural and Cross-Country Pipelines	80	Ship Channel Design
47	Selected Abstracts on Structural Applications of Plastics	81	Guidelines for Cloud Seeding to Augment Precipitation
49	Urban Planning Guide	82	Odor Control in Wastewater Treatment Plants
50	Planning and Design Guidelines for Small Craft Harbors	83	Environmental Site Investigation
51	Survey of Current Structural Research	84	Mechanical Connections in Wood Structures
52	Guide for the Design of Steel Transmission Towers	85	Quality of Ground Water
53	Criteria for Maintenance of Multilane Highways	86	Operation and Maintenance of Ground Water Facilities
55	Guide to Employment Conditions for Civil Engineers	87	Urban Runoff Quality Manual
57	Management, Operation and Maintenance of Irrigation and Drainage Systems	88	Management of Water Treatment Plant Residuals
59	Computer Pricing Practices	89	Pipeline Crossings
60	Gravity Sanitary Sewer Design and Construction	90	Guide to Structural Optimization
62	Existing Sewer Evaluation and Rehabilitation	91	Design of Guyed Electrical Transmission Structures
63	Structural Plastics Design Manual	92	Manhole Inspection and Rehabilitation
64	Manual on Engineering Surveying	93	Crane Safety on Construction Sites
65	Construction Cost Control	94	Inland Navigation: Locks, Dams, and Channels
66	Structural Plastics Selection Manual	95	Urban Subsurface Drainage
67	Wind Tunnel Studies of Buildings and Structures	96	Guide to Improved Earthquake Performance of Electric Power Systems
68	Aeration: A Wastewater Treatment Process	97	Hydraulic Modeling: Concepts and Practice
69	Sulfide in Wastewater Collection and Treatment Systems	98	Conveyance of Residuals from Water and Wastewater Treatment
70	Evapotranspiration and Irrigation Water Requirements	99	Environmental Site Characterization and Remediation Design Guidance
71	Agricultural Salinity Assessment and Management	100	Groundwater Contamination by Organic Pollutants: Analysis and Remediation
72	Design of Steel Transmission Pole Structures	101	Underwater Investigations
		102	Design Guide for FRP Composite Connections
		103	Guide to Hiring and Retaining Great Civil Engineers

FOREWORD

The American Society of Civil Engineers (ASCE) has been concerned with procedures for engaging engineering services since the early 1900s. The first ASCE manual on the subject was published in 1930. The designation *Manual No. 45–A Guide for the Engagement of Engineering Services* was adopted in 1964, with revised editions issued in 1972, 1975, 1981, 1988, and 1996. This manual is the 2002 edition. It has been renamed *Manual No. 45–How to Work Effectively with Consulting Engineers: Getting the Best Project at the Right Price.*

This manual is intended to outline the functions of the consulting engineer in serving a client, explain the types of services usually offered, provide various methods of determining compensation for engineering services, and provide the general ranges of remuneration received by competent consulting engineers for their services. A recommended procedure for interviewing and selecting a consulting engineer and guidance on contracts for engineering services are also provided. This work is designed to serve the best interests of both the client and the consulting engineer and to foster better understanding between them. The information offered is intended to apply to civil engineering practice, but certain aspects of this manual may not be applicable to specialty practice.

A survey questionnaire, prepared by the ASCE Task Committee on the Update of Manual 45, was sent in early 2000 to consulting engineering firms whose assistance was requested to update and improve this manual. Usable responses were received from over 300 firms. This Task Committee evaluated the results of the survey together with other suggestions in preparing this edition.

It is to be understood that the historical data presented herein for engineering charges, percentage fees, factors on payrolls, etc., are not to be considered as fixed, or maximum, or minimum—but rather as general guides to be used or not used, at the sole discretion of each user, to assist in evaluating compensation negotiated between clients and consulting engineers. The data provide a sound basis for such evaluations and negotiations, since they are based on the experience of many consulting engineers as obtained in the recent national survey.

The Task Committee gratefully acknowledges those firms and individuals that contributed their time and talent to make the revised manual better able to serve the public, the client, and the profession.

ACKNOWLEDGMENTS

**ASCE Committee on Practice Guidelines
of the Committee on Professional Practice**

Howard C. Begbie, Chairman, 2002

Rich Hovey
Rodney P. Plourde
Lloyd H. Woosley
Gary A. Parks

ASCE Task Committee for the Update of Manual 45

Gary A. Parks, Chairman

Roland "Buzz" Berger
David F. Garber
Susan M. Hann
Jack R. Roadhouse

ASCE Staff Contact
John J. Segna

The Task Committee for the Update of Manual No. 45 developed the survey questionnaire to solicit from consulting engineering firms and prepared the text for this revised edition of Manual No. 45.

CONTENTS

Foreword   v

1 The Practice of Engineering   1

2 Classification of Engineering Services   9

3 Selecting the Engineer 19

4 Methods of Charging for Engineering Services 29

5 Total Project Cost 41

6 Contracts for Engineering Services 47

Appendix 1   EJCDC Documents 55

Appendix 2   Engineer Selection Process—Typical Forms 61

Glossary 69

Index 77

Chapter 1

THE PRACTICE OF ENGINEERING

During the next decade, billions of dollars will be spent to improve the infrastructure at the local, state, and federal levels. The American Society of Civil Engineers (ASCE) is dedicated to advancing the highest standards in civil engineering to achieve quality-built projects that best utilize taxpayer dollars. Most of these projects will be developed by government agencies working closely with consultants. In addition, billions more will be spent by private clients working in conjunction with civil engineers.

Civil engineering consulting firms serve as an adjunct to public agency and private corporations when extra staffing or greater expertise on particular projects is required. This manual was developed to help all civil engineering clients—from seasoned public agency professionals to those supervising their first public works project—work more effectively with their civil engineering consultants to achieve quality results.

The manual covers all facets of working with a civil engineering consulting firm; major topics include range of services available, contract delivery systems, typical costs for services, and how to select and work effectively with a consulting firm. This guide is intended for use primarily with design-bid-build projects, including new construction or modification of existing facilities with construction costs up to $10 million.

QUALITY

This manual provides a guide to procuring engineering services for a quality project. Quality entails meeting client expectations as well as project specifications. Quality does not just happen; it must be designed into every aspect of the project. This requires dedication, effort, and adequate time for investigation, planning, and innovation. To achieve this result, the consultant must be compensated fairly and receive

1

appropriate authority and responsibility to do the job. Additionally, clear communication between the client and the consultant is required to understand the client's needs and the options open to the consultant.

Quality results from a team effort and is measured largely by the degree of satisfaction of all parties involved. This manual is dedicated to advancing both the understanding and quality of the practice of engineering and extending the standard of care of the profession of civil engineering. (See ASCE *Manual No. 73, Quality in the Constructed Project, Second Edition.*)

PROFESSIONAL RESPONSIBILITY

Engineers typically are given responsibility for studying, conceiving, designing, managing, and inspecting construction. They are also asked to help establish operating and maintenance standards for engineered works. The need for other services may arise on occasion during the evolution of a project. The health, safety, well being, and comfort of the public using the facility and the ultimate facility cost all depend on how well members of the engineering team fulfill their contractual responsibilities. Therefore, the engineer has obligations as trustee to the public interest as well as the private interests of clients. Successfully fulfilling these responsibilities requires candor, mutual trust, effective communication, and understanding between the consultant and the client. Only in this way can a professional relationship be established and the project be completed successfully.

CLIENT–CONSULTANT RELATIONSHIPS

Many engineering works are conceived, designed, and constructed through the efforts of practicing engineers employed in governmental agencies or in industry. Other engineering projects come to fruition through the efforts of an independent consulting firm engaged for a specific project or program by a public agency or private client. Many municipalities and private companies rely on independent consultants to accomplish projects that require special expertise or to help handle an overload of work on their existing staff.

In addition, clients have started using new concepts, such as program management, design-build/turnkey, and design-build-operate-and-maintain (DBOM) to implement projects. With a clear understanding of the project needs, the client and consultant can determine which concept is right for a particular project. Traditionally, the client–consultant relationship stipulates the client as the owner and the consultant as the employee responsible for delivering the desired product to the owner. Concepts such as DBOM make the consultant a shared owner. The definition and explanation of proper relationships between consultants and their public and private clients are important objectives of this manual.

ENGINEERING SERVICES

Independent engineering consulting firms can provide a host of important services to their public or private clients. These services are explored in depth in Chapter 2. Typical services include the following:

- consultations and advice
- feasibility studies
- field investigations and engineering data collection
- environmental assessments and impact statements
- engineering reports
- estimates of probable construction cost
- preliminary and final designs, drawings, specifications, and construction bidding documents
- assistance in securing construction bids and awarding contracts
- construction administration and observation
- arrangements for or performance of materials and equipment testing
- assistance in startup, assessment of capacity, and operation of facilities
- preparation of operation and maintenance manuals
- appraisals and rate studies
- value engineering
- expert testimony
- provision of supplemental temporary staff

Consulting engineers also may serve as construction managers, program managers, or operations and maintenance managers, and may employ other consultants and contractors as part of their services.

Many consultants specialize in specific areas of engineering—e.g., field and photogrammetric surveying, geotechnical, structural, civil, environmental, mechanical, or electrical—while other firms offer diversified services in several disciplines of engineering. Consultants draw upon the combined talents of economists, planners, engineers and designers, estimators, architects, scientists, technical analysts, specification writers, field representatives, surveyors, and others.

The consultant provides services that may result in the client committing financial resources for construction of a proposed project. The client, who may be unfamiliar with the technical and engineering aspects of the project, must often accept at face value the suitability of the constructed project for the intended function. Thus, it is vital that the consultant and the client agree upon the project budget from the onset. If the budget will not produce a product that realistically meets client expectations, the consultant must clarify this matter. Although consultants cannot guarantee the outcome of final construction price, they will make decisions that affect the final price and, therefore, must work closely with the client to ensure that the final costs are in line with expectations. Thus, consulting services must be performed in a competent and efficient manner, employing a high degree of professionalism and ethics, and in an atmosphere of mutual respect and trust.

PROJECT IMPLEMENTATION APPROACHES

Project implementation has become increasingly complex, involving financial, environmental, regulatory, technical, and managerial matters. As a result, clients have opted to pursue a number of implementation approaches.

One approach commonly used is called *program management.* Under program management, clients recognize that they do not have the expertise to pull together all of the elements required to complete a project. The client retains a program manager to perform specialized tasks necessary to develop or construct a specific project. Moreover, the client may retain a program manager to develop, define, and oversee the program; prepare budgetary estimates of program costs; prepare program schedules; evaluate and select members of the program team; and provide periodic program status reports. In other cases, the program manager's staff interacts with—and serves as an extension of—the client's staff throughout the life of the program. In most cases, the client continues to be the contracting agent with all members of the program team and the contractors hired to construct the project. The program manager acts as the facilitator and assumes whatever responsibilities and authority the client wishes to delegate in order to achieve a successful project.

Other approaches include design-build/turnkey and design-build-operate-and-maintain (DBOM). With design-build, the owner provides a concept of the desired project, and a team of designers and builders combine to engineer and construct the entire project and return it to the client upon completion (i.e., ready to "turn the key"). Under DBOM, the designbuilder takes on the additional responsibilities of operation and maintenance for a specified period of time and thus acts as an owner/operator during that time frame. DBOM is selected typically when a client is interested in privatizing a program and is therefore interested in having the DBOM team finance all or a portion of the project to offset local client readily available funding.

SELECTING A CONSULTING ENGINEER

Selecting a consultant is one of the most important decisions in the project development process. Your ability to meet your objectives—including the effective use of financial resources, soundness of design, and suitability of the proposed project for its intended function—rests upon the experience, organization, skill, integrity, and judgment of the consultant. The consultant's recommendations affect life-cycle costs and thereby influence the project's economic feasibility.

Engineering services constitute only a small percentage of the life-cycle cost for most construction projects—typically less than 1% to 2% of total cost. Therefore, engaging the most qualified and reputable consulting firm available is in the client's best interest. In addition, it usually is best for the client to select a consultant who can support the project from conception through design, construction, and project startup. This continuity helps to build a solid relationship between the consultant and the client and adds to the success of the project.

Qualifications, experience, reputation, and quality of client service are critically important in selecting a consultant. Selection based primarily on cost of services, with limited consideration to competence or expertise, can result in unsatisfactory service to the client and higher overall project costs. The consultant's competence in specialty fields, performance on similar projects, interrelationship with the design team members, personnel assignments, provision for independent reviews, and quality assurance all influence the construction, operation, and maintenance costs; insurance and other annual charges; and the resulting life-cycle costs of the project. ASCE recommends that a client engage a consultant in two steps. The first step is based on qualifications vital to the project. Because selecting an engineer based on quality and expertise is somewhat subjective, screening should be performed by individuals in the client's organization who are best suited to the task.

Once a consultant is selected, the next step is to define the scope and expectations of the engineering services to be provided. This step must be completed before negotiating a fee for services. A clearly defined scope of services greatly reduces the potential for misunderstandings or confusion that can later evolve into project delays and claims for additional compensation. A detailed scope of services protects the interests of both the client and the consultant.

ASCE supports procedures such as those specified by the Brooks Act (P.L. 92–582) and the American Bar Association's Model Procurement Code for State and Local Governments for the engagement of engineering services. In applying these procedures, the selection, procurement, and administration of engineering services should be the responsibility of the owner or the owner's engineering staff.[1]

PRIME PROFESSIONAL PRACTICE

The guidelines in this manual refer specifically to the engagement of engineering services in which the consultant serves the client directly as a prime professional and in which the client is usually the owner of the project. Some sections are also applicable when a consultant serves the client indirectly as a subconsultant through another engineer or architect who is serving as the prime professional. Although the consultant might be a prime professional or joint venture partner on design-build or DBOM contracts, more often the consultant is a subconsultant to a contractor who serves as the prime professional.

DESIGN COMPETITION

In a design competition, one consultant is selected over others based on an innovative approach to solving the client's needs. Design competitions usually are reserved for significant programs such as signature bridges. Because this type of project is as important for the competing consulting firms as for the client, the firms may spend a significant amount of time and effort in pursuit of this work. As a result, all competing consultants should be awarded a stipend to participate in the competition and, in addition, should be compensated for their costs. As the stipend generally will be small in comparison to expenditures, final selection criteria should be well specified. A subjective selection process may limit the number of firms willing to commit resources to compete for the project. Competing firms are normally identified from the consultants' response to the client's solicitation letter or notice in a newspaper or trade publication.

CONTINGENCY BASIS OF EMPLOYMENT

Canon 5c of the ASCE Code of Ethics provides that "Engineers may request, propose, or accept professional commissions on a contingent

---

[1] ASCE Policy Statement #304, Qualifications-Based Selection of Professional Engineers, April 12, 1999.

basis only under circumstances in which their professional judgments would not be compromised."[2] Although contingent commissions are permissible, ASCE believes it is not generally in the best interest of the client or the public for the consultant to provide professional services on a contingency basis.

Similarly, it is the opinion of ASCE that it is not in the client's best interest to use a contingency basis for professional engagements such as expert witness service, up-front engineering studies, and designs for a developer's project, or patent engineering where the consultant's compensation is dependent on a successful venture or court finding.

SUMMARY

The foundation for a successful project begins with an appropriate working relationship developed between the client and the consulting engineer. Developing a professional and trusting relationship is essential to ensuring that the project satisfies the client's needs and is accomplished within the agreed schedule and budget.

---

[2] ASCE Code of Ethics, available online at <www.asce.org/inside/ethics.cfm>.

Chapter 2

CLASSIFICATION OF ENGINEERING SERVICES

The need for professional engineering services varies along with the organizational structure, size, and capability of consulting engineering firms. Many consulting engineering firms provide comprehensive services, while other firms specialize in specific areas of engineering—such as geotechnical, environmental, traffic, or structural—and provide their services to a prime engineer, architect, or owner. Few consulting firms are qualified to provide complete service for all projects; thus, it is common to use associate consulting professionals to provide specialized services.

The services provided by consultants can be grouped into the following three broad categories:

1. Consultations, investigations, and studies,
2. Services relating to construction projects, and
3. Special services

This chapter provides a description of the types of services that a consultant may be expected to provide a client. However, the classification of services is not nearly as important as the mutual understanding of services required between the consultant and the client. It is imperative that the consultant and client communicate clearly about the scope of services needed.

Both parties must clearly understand what services are and are not included. Frequently, a client may assume that services, such as extra meetings, are included in the cost when it is the intention of the engineer to charge additional fees. Conversely, the engineer may want to decline responsibility for inspecting construction. To remove doubt, clarifying language should be included in the contract for engineering services.

Consultation, Investigations, and Studies

Consultants may be engaged to provide consulting services or to conduct various types of studies or investigations. These services primarily deal with collecting, interpreting, and reporting information, as well as formulating conclusions and making recommendations. Typical services in this category include the following.

Preliminary and Feasibility Investigations and Reports

These services usually precede the authorization of a capital project and may involve extensive investigations, analyses of conditions, and comparisons of several possible plans. They may focus on alternatives analysis, environmental impact, sustainable development, operating costs, life-cycle costs, financing considerations, and expected revenues as bases for conclusions and recommendations regarding the advisability of undertaking a project.

Planning Studies

These services include the broad areas of developing master plans for long-range capital improvement programs; preparation of land development plans, urban plans, and regional plans; and the investigation of environmental conditions and preparation of environmental impact studies, with subsequent planning to improve or maintain existing conditions. Such planning often requires coordination of the work of engineering and other disciplines.

Public Involvement

The client may engage the engineer to present a project concept, technical analysis, or planning study to the public. In addition, the client may use the engineer to solicit public involvement on a particular project or study. These services require the engineer to be familiar with the array of public involvement techniques in order to achieve the desired result.

Appraisals, Valuations, and Rate Studies

These services may include investigations and analyses of existing conditions; estimates of capital and operating costs, overhead costs, and financing costs; and forecasts of revenues for property development or for the recommendation of prospective utility rates.

Assistance in Financial Matters

A client who is planning to issue bonds—particularly revenue bonds—to finance a capital project may engage a consultant. The scope of services may include an evaluation of capabilities of existing and proposed facilities to meet present and projected future needs, statements of probable construction costs, and an estimate of annual revenue requirements, as well as a determination of appropriate rates to provide this income. The consultant also may act as the responsible agent to certify that certain terms and conditions of the bond issues are carried out.

Materials Engineering and Equipment Tests

These services include tests of materials and equipment under established codes and standards, specialized examination of equipment and materials used in construction and industry, and other inspections and monitoring required by the clients.

Inspections and Evaluations of Existing Facilities and Structures

These inspections include material testing for a bridge, sewage treatment plant, airport runway, and other facilities or structures.

Direct Personal Services

This includes services such as assistance in preparing for legal proceedings, appearances before courts or commissions to render expert opinions and conclusions, and investigation of technical matters in which specialized engineering knowledge, experience, and judgment are required.

CONSTRUCTION PROJECTS

Professional engineering services are required for each of the six typical phases of a construction project. Ideally, for consistency and efficiency, all services should be provided by the same consultant, although at times services in various phases can be furnished by different consultants or by the client.

The six standard phases of a construction project and the engineering services needed for each are as follows.

1. *Study and Report Phase*—analysis of client needs, evaluation of alternatives and recommendations of a preferred option, conceptual design, conceptual opinions of probable construction cost
2. *Preliminary Design Phase*—preparation of final design criteria, preliminary drawings, outline specifications, and preliminary estimate of construction cost

3. *Final Design Phase*—preparation of construction drawings, specifications, estimates of probable construction cost, and other contract documents
4. *Bidding or Negotiating Phase*—assistance to the client with the bidding or negotiating process for construction of the project
5. *Construction Phase*—representation of the client during construction and inspection of construction
6. *Operation Phase*—assistance to the client in startup and operation of the project, including periodic inspections

In some cases, the study and report phase, the preliminary design phase, and the final design phase may be combined, especially for smaller projects. Although the client often will specify what phases of service are required, the engineer also may offer advice about the appropriate steps needed for the project.

More detailed descriptions of the six phases follow.

Study and Report Phase

This phase involves determination of project scope and economic and technical evaluation of feasible alternatives. The services performed during this phase may include the following:

- Review available data and consult with the client to clarify and define project requirements.
- Advise the client about the need to provide or obtain additional data or services, and assist the client in obtaining them. These additional services may include photogrammetry, reconnaissance surveys, property surveys, topographic surveys, geotechnical investigations and consultations, compilation of hydrological data, traffic studies, materials engineering, assembly of zoning, deed and other restrictive land use information, and environmental assessments and impact statements.
- Identify and analyze requirements of governmental authorities that have jurisdiction to approve the design of the project, and participate in consultations with such authorities.
- Identify and analyze pertinent government regulations and work with government agencies as needed to ensure that the design specifications meet with their approval.
- Provide analyses of the client's needs, planning surveys, and comparative evaluations of prospective sites and solutions.
- Provide a general economic analysis of various alternatives that meet the client's requirements.
- Present the project concepts and alternatives to obtain input from the public or affected citizens and businesses.

- Prepare a report that includes alternative solutions available to the client as well as the consultant's findings and recommendations. The report may contain schematic layouts, sketches, conceptual design criteria with appropriate exhibits indicating clearly the considerations involved (including applicable requirements of governmental authorities having jurisdiction), and the consultant's conceptual opinion of probable costs for the project.

Preliminary Design Phase

This phase establishes the general size and scope of the project and its location on the selected site. Services may include the following:

- Consult with the client, review preliminary reports, clarify and define project requirements, review available data, and discuss general scheduling. Conferences with approving and regulatory governmental agencies and applicable utilities also may be required.
- Advise the client about requirements for additional data or services described in the study and report phase, and assist the client in obtaining such data and services.
- Prepare preliminary design documents, including final design criteria, preliminary drawings, outline specifications, and written descriptions of the project.
- Determine right-of-way and easement needs.
- Present the project to the public or to affected citizens/businesses.
- Prepare revised opinions of probable total project costs.
- Provide periodic status reports.

Final Design Phase

This phase of project development is usually undertaken only after the client has approved the preliminary design phase material. The basic services for the final design phase may include the following:

- Prepare construction drawings and specifications showing the character and extent of the project based on the accepted preliminary design documents.
- Prepare right-of-way and easement documents.
- Prepare and present a revised estimate of probable total project costs based on the final drawings and specifications.
- Furnish the necessary engineering data and assist in the application for regulatory permits from local, state, or federal authorities. These are distinguished from and do not include detailed applications and supporting documents for government grants-in-aid or planning

grants that would be furnished as additional services, described later in this chapter.

- Prepare basic documents related to construction contracts for review and approval by the client and the client's legal and other advisors. These may include contract agreement forms, general conditions and supplementary conditions, invitations to bid, instructions to bidders, insurance and bonding requirements, and other contract-related documents.
- Furnish the client a specified number of copies of drawings, specifications, and other contract documents.
- Present the project to the public or to affected citizens and businesses.
- Provide periodic status reports.

Bidding or Negotiating Phase

Services under this phase may include the following:

- Assist the client in advertising and obtaining bids or negotiating proposals for each separate prime construction contract, maintain a record of prospective bidders to whom bidding documents have been issued, attend pre-bid conferences, and receive and process deposits for bidding documents.
- Issue addenda as appropriate to interpret, clarify, expand, or amend the bidding documents.
- Assist the client in determining the qualifications and acceptability of prospective contractors, subcontractors, and materials suppliers.
- Advise the client on the acceptability of alternative materials and equipment proposed by the prospective constructors when substitution prior to the award of contracts is allowed by the bidding documents.
- Attend the bid opening, prepare bid tabulation sheets, and assist the client in evaluating bids or proposals and in assembling and awarding contracts for construction, materials, equipment, and services.

Construction Phase

Services performed during this phase are those usually associated with acting as the client's representative. Construction services may include:

- Review, for compliance with design concepts, the shop and erection drawings submitted by the constructors.
- Review laboratory, shop, and mill test reports on materials and equipment, or provide inspection at the manufacturing facilities during the production of materials specific to the project.

- Visit the project site at appropriate intervals as construction proceeds to observe and report on the progress and the quality of the executed work.
- Provide services of a full-time resident project representative, and support staff as required, during construction to ensure that it is accomplished in conformance with the construction drawings, specifications, and other contract documents.
- Issue instructions from the client to the contractors, issue necessary interpretations and clarifications of contract documents, prepare change orders requiring special inspections and testing of the work, and make recommendations as to acceptability of the work.
- Make recommendations to the client on corrective actions or contractual measures that may be exercised by the owner.
- Prepare sketches required to resolve problems due to actual field conditions encountered.
- Determine amounts of progress payments due, based on degree of completion of the work, and recommend issuance of such payments by the client.
- Observe and assist performance tests and initial operation of the project.
- Prepare record drawings from information submitted by the contractor or resident engineer.
- Make a final inspection and report on completion of the project, including recommendations concerning final payments to contractors and release of retained percentages.

Operation Phase

At the completion of construction, as a basic service the consultant may assist with the startup of project operations. The consultant may be commissioned to prepare a manual for both operation and maintenance requirements, and may also provide assistance in adjusting and balancing equipment, identifying deficiencies and assisting in obtaining corrections, and performing inspection prior to the end of the project warranty period. The consultant may assist in operator training, setting up job classifications and salaries, organizing the purchase of supplies, developing charts for recording operational data, and observing and reporting on project operations.

SPECIAL SERVICES

Special services required during the study, design, construction, and operation phases of a construction project may include investigations, reports, and activities beyond the scope of the basic services. These services, many of which are also listed earlier in this chapter under the category "Consultations, Investigations, and Studies," relate to feasibility, scope, and location of the project. The research, compilation of engineering data, and acquisition of property may involve professional specialists in engineering and other fields.

Special services that may be provided by the consultant, or negotiated with other firms or subconsultants by the consultant acting on behalf of the client, include the following.

- Geotechnical engineering—including test borings, sampling and analysis, and recommendations.
- Special studies, tests, and process determinations to establish design criteria or demonstrate compliance.
- Land surveys, establishment of boundaries and monuments, preparation of easement descriptions, and related computations and drawings.
- Engineering and topographic surveys for design and construction.
- Mill, shop, or laboratory inspections of the materials and equipment.
- Additional copies of reports, construction drawings, specifications, and other documents as required for bidding and construction beyond the number specified in the basic services agreement.
- Extra travel and subsistence as defined by the agreement for engineering services.
- Value engineering—including review of the work of other engineers, either within the same organization or in other firms, to determine whether a proposed solution is optimum and, if not, to suggest a better approach for meeting the project's functional and financial criteria.
- Redesign to reflect changes requested by the client or necessitated by the client's acceptance of substitutions proposed by the contractor.
- Assistance to the client as an expert witness in litigation in connection with the project or in hearings before approving and regulatory agencies.
- Final investigations involving detailed consideration of operation, maintenance, and overhead expenses, and preparation of final rate schedules and earning and expense statements, appraisals, valuations, and material audits or inventories required for certification of force account construction performed by the client or for extra work done by the contractor.
- Preparation of detailed applications and supporting documents for government grants or advances for public works projects.
- Plotting, computing, and filing subdivision plats staking lots, and other land planning and partitioning activities.

- Preparation of environmental assessment and impact statements and other assistance to the client in connection with public hearings.
- Additional studies and design efforts to meet special conditions encountered during construction.
- Assistance in the selection and engagement of architects, other engineers, contractors, and subcontractors; review and approval of their work; contacting governmental agencies to obtain permits and documents; and other services related to project development.
- Assessment of completed project's ability to meet its design intent.

Chapter 3

SELECTING THE ENGINEER

The selection and engagement of a consultant is the most crucial decision the client will make when planning a new engineering project. No two consulting firms have the same training, experience, capabilities, personnel, or workloads. Selection of the most qualified firm for a specific project will result in a well-planned and designed, economical, and successful project.

BASIS FOR SELECTION

The client should establish administrative policy and criteria for the selection of qualified consultants for particular projects. The client's first step is to define the scope of the proposed project. In some cases this may be a general statement of performance requirements. At other times the tasks to be performed may be individually identified and defined. By clearly defining the services that the consultant is expected to furnish, the client can accurately judge which firm is best equipped to provide them.

The following factors are among those to consider in the selection process.

- *Ethical Reputation.* The professional and ethical reputation of the consulting firm and staff should be determined by inquiries to previous clients and other references.
- *Licensed Professional Engineers.* Responsible employees of the consulting firm must be registered professional engineers in the state of operation and/or registered in the states in which they practice engineering for the firm.
- *Experience.* The consulting firm should have demonstrated qualifications and expertise in performing the services required for the project.

- *Staff.* The consultant should be able to assign qualified engineering staff to take charge of the project and provide the required services within the time allotted.
- *Financial Resources.* The consultant should have the necessary financial resources to accomplish the assignment and provide continuing service.
- *Current Technology.* The consultant should be current with technology, including computer software and hardware and other supporting equipment.

SELECTION COMMITTEE

The client should have an established administrative policy for designating individuals authorized to select or recommend selection of consultants for specific assignments. Those assigned to select consultants can be appropriate administrators, department heads, or both, possibly supplemented by a selection team or committee. Those appointed should be familiar with the project requirements and should remain free of internal or external pressure during the selection process.

Using a committee of three or more individuals, including at least one professional engineer of the appropriate discipline, can be an effective way to select consultants. The client's project manager also should be included. For public projects, the client must choose individuals who demonstrate objectivity in order to avoid any appearance of a conflict of interest in the selection process. At least one of the individuals should be thoroughly familiar with consulting practices. The committee is responsible for making recommendations after conducting appropriate investigations, interviews, and inquiries. The final selection by the client's administrator or governing body is then based upon the selection committee's recommendations.

STATEMENT OF QUALIFICATIONS FILE

The qualifications of the prospective consultants should be the primary focus of the selection process. Many large industrial firms and land development companies, practically all branches of the federal government, and many state, county, and municipal agencies that engage consultants maintain a file of "Statements of Qualifications" for firms providing various types of engineering services. Such data often are presented in a standard form, in brochures, or through a combination of both.

Federal agencies and many others use U.S. government Form SF 254 Architect-Engineer and Related Services Questionnaire as a standard statement of qualifications. This form can be obtained from the Office of Federal Acquisition and Regulatory Policy, GSA, Washington, D.C. 20405, or accessed online at <http://contacts.gsa.gov/webforms.ns> (click on "Standard" and go to SF254).

The following information should be included in a statement of qualifications.

- Name and address of firm
- Telephone and fax numbers and e-mail address
- Name of person to contact
- Services provided
- Number of personnel by specialty, including the number registered as professional engineers or registered land surveyors
- Completed projects for which the firm was the engineer of record, including at least one project for each specialty offered
- Estimated annual capacity based on revenue dollars
- Banking references
- Brochures or other promotional information provided at the discretion of the consultant
- Client references

QUALIFICATIONS-BASED SELECTION (QBS) PROCEDURE

The selection procedure is more effective when the client can describe the project in detail and can prepare a project scope and outline of services expected from the consultant. In some cases, the client may not have professional staff available to define the project scope and describe the required services. In any event, the client should still be familiar enough with the project requirements to understand what is expected of the consultant. The selection procedure, however, can be modified to suit particular circumstances.

At each stage of the evaluation, prospective consultants should be informed of the qualifications/selection criteria that are important to the client and how they will be rated. A matrix should be developed that lists the items of importance and the weight to be given to each.

Typical steps in the selection procedure are presented below. If the client has had a satisfactory experience with one or more consultants, it may not be necessary to follow all of the steps outlined.

Requests for Qualifications

By invitation, using qualification file information, or by public announcement, issue a Request for Qualifications (RFQ) from consultants.

Information requested should be specified in the consultants' Statement of Qualifications and might include the following:

- Proposed project staff with short-form resumes
- Similar projects completed by the firm
- Anticipated workload versus capacity during proposed project duration
- Other information at the consultant's discretion. U.S. government Form SF255 Architect-Engineer and Related Services Questionnaire for Specific Projects (see "Statement of Qualifications File" above) is sometimes used as a standard for submitting this information. Encourage consultants to streamline the information contained in their response and to focus on the items requested
- Guidelines on how consultant questions regarding the project will be handled. Normally, questions should be in writing with responses also in writing and given to all consultants proposing on the project

Short List

Select at least three firms that appear to be best qualified for the specific project. Often more than three firms might appear to be equally qualified, in which case more firms can be considered. However, in view of the cost and time required by consultants to prepare competent proposals, it is usually best to make a conscientious effort to keep the number selected to a realistic minimum. Check with each firm's recent clients to determine the quality of their performance. This check need not be limited to references listed by the consultant.

Request for Proposal (RFP)

Write a letter requesting a proposal to each firm selected for further consideration. This letter should describe the proposed project in detail, delineate the project scope, provide an outline of services required, and, if available, present the terms and conditions of the contract. This letter also should tell the consultant what is required in the proposal; required elements should include the following:

- Consulting engineer's plan for managing and performing the required services,
- Proposed project manager and qualifications,
- Key personnel to be assigned to the project and their qualifications,
- Proposed schedule,
- Experience with similar projects,
- Office location in which services are to be performed,

- Financial stability,
- Present workload, and
- References.

In some situations, it may be desirable to request some of this more detailed information with the statement of qualifications.

Each firm should have an opportunity to visit the site, review all pertinent data, and obtain clarification of any items as required. For major or particularly complex projects, a preproposal conference to explain details of the proposed scope of services and to answer questions can be beneficial.

Evaluation and Selection

Upon receipt of proposals, invite the firms to meet individually with the selection committee for an interview and to discuss the desired end results of the project and the engineering services required. These interviews can be held either at the client's or the consultant's office. The client may consider supplementing the selection committee with personnel who have specialized expertise to advise the committee. During each interview, the selection committee should review the qualifications and experience of each firm, technical capability, staff capacity to provide the services within the time allotted, key personnel to be assigned to the project, and the consultant's approach to satisfying the project requirements. The consultant should address quality control and quality assurance. The proposed project manager should be present at the interview and should have a prominent role in the consultant's presentation.

After all interviews have been conducted, list the firms in the order of preference, taking into account their approach and understanding of the project, reputation, experience, financial standing, size, available personnel and project management, quality of references, workload, location, and other factors pertinent to the project being considered.

Invite the consultant considered to be best qualified to develop a detailed scope, list of deliverables, and schedule, and negotiate fair compensation for the services. Inform the selected consultant of the method of compensation proposed for his services (see Chapter 4). It also may be advisable to schedule a meeting with the selected firm to address any concerns or questions about specific project requirements.

Evaluate the compensation proposed by the consultant on the basis of the client's experience and budget estimate, taking into account the range of charges for engineering services (reported in Chapter 5). Give consideration to the project's special characteristics and the agreed upon scope of services. Providing fair and reasonable compensation to the consultant is vital to the success of the project, as it will enable the consultant's expertise to be fully utilized.

If a satisfactory agreement is not reached with the first selected consultant, negotiations should be terminated and the firm notified in writing. Similar negotiations should then be held with the second-ranked firm and, if necessary, sequentially by ranking with the other firms until a satisfactory agreement is reached. This procedure usually results in the development of a satisfactory contract. If no accord is reached, the client should seek outside assistance from an independent consultant before continuing with the selection process. All such negotiations should be on a strictly confidential basis; compensation arrangements discussed with one consultant should never be disclosed to another.

Contract

When agreement has been reached on scope, schedule, and compensation, the client and selected consultant should formalize their agreement in a written contract conforming to the guidelines in Chapter 6. Both parties should execute the contract, and the consultant should be given a notice to proceed with the work. Appendix 2 of this Manual contains typical forms for various activities in the selection process.

HELPFUL SUGGESTIONS FOR THE SELECTION PROCESS

Some valuable practical tips on hiring a consultant include the following.

- A poorly defined scope of required services can result in numerous change orders. Clearly define what is needed from the consultant.
- Forms SF 254 and SF 255 compartmentalize information about the firm. Both can be valuable tools when used correctly. For example, a consultant might indicate that it has 600 employees; however, 596 of these employees might be located in another state. Determine which staff members are local and available for the project.
- Check the ability of the consultant to concentrate on your project. Are there other projects and demands that could take priority?
- Insist on talking to the engineers who will be assigned to your project, especially the engineer who will be dealing with the public.
- When issuing an RFP or RFQ, define what you want to know and limit the response to this information. Reject proposals that do not respond to these specific instructions.
- Ensure that competing firms are not lobbying selection committee members or elected officials. Establish one point of contact, such as a purchasing employee who is not on the selection committee, to perform administrative functions and to conduct all interactions with the prospective firms. This person can neutrally answer questions and ensure that all firms receive the same information.

- Assess the level of professional liability insurance needed. If it is more than the consultant normally carries, the client may be required to reimburse the consultant for the added cost.
- Ask for a breakdown of who performs quality control and quality assurance and what percentage of the time/cost is devoted to each.
- Consider engaging the engineer's services during construction. The engineer could be helpful in the bidding process and construction administration, and could serve as the client representative. The consultant also could be helpful in resolving construction problems in the field. If these services are required, the consultant should be compensated accordingly.
- Have your attorney review the contract documents.

PROCEDURE FOR OPEN-END CONTRACT

An "open-end" contract for engineering services is used to supplement a client's staff or to provide services for several specific projects. Staff requirements or projects may or may not be completely known at the time of the announcement for consultant services. The contract normally will provide an "upset figure" or "not-to-exceed amount" for consultants' fees or specify a number of hours for each discipline.

Clients can add consultant staff to supplement in-house staff or add disciplines that are not available in-house. Consultant compensation normally is based on a schedule of hourly rates specified in the contract.

Fees are negotiable for each individual project under the "upset figure" specified in the contract. On occasion, the negotiation of fees can be bypassed prior to initiating the work, such as in cases of emergency.

The selection process is similar to that given for QBS procedure in the previous section. The announcement of the project will specify the required engineering disciplines, the number of hours, or an "upset figure" for fees. For multiple project services, the announcement will specify the general nature of the work and could include specific information on the initial project to be undertaken. The consultant is expected to respond with background staff, similar experience, availability of staff, and other pertinent information.

BIDDING

Many federal and state agencies, as well as professional engineering and architectural societies, recognize QBS as the preferred method for procurement of professional services. In fact, most states and the federal government have adopted laws that require the procurement of professional engineering and architectural services only by a process similar to that for the QBS procedure described above. ASCE believes that the selection of professional engineers as prime consultants and subconsultants should result from competition based on the qualifications best suited to complete the work successfully. Qualifications—including the training, registration, experience, skills, and availability of the proposed project personnel—are paramount in engaging engineering services. Cost of engineering services, while important and meriting careful negotiations and performance accountability, is related to work to be performed, which often is not clearly defined at the time the engineer is selected. Therefore, cost should be secondary to professional qualifications.[3]

There are many reasons why bidding for consulting services often produces unsatisfactory results for the client. Principal among these are the following.

- *Professional Judgment.* Bidding does not recognize professional judgment, which is the key difference between professional services and the furnishing of products. Judgment is an essential ingredient in quality engineering services.
- *Incomplete Scope.* It is virtually impossible to completely detail the scope of services required for an engineering project in advance— especially in the study and preliminary phases—without lengthy discussions and negotiations with the selected firm. In the attempt to stay competitive while lacking specifics, the bidding firms must submit a price for the least effort envisioned. The resulting service performed is likely to be tailored to fit the minimal requirements of the bid documents and will not necessarily suit the client's needs or expectations. As a result, the client will be required to negotiate fees for extra services not initially envisioned.
- *Minimum Service.* In-depth studies and analyses by the consultant are not likely to be performed. The consultant selected by lowest bid often will provide only the minimum services necessary to satisfy the client's scope of services.
- *Lack of Detail.* The engineering designs are likely to be minimal in completeness, with the details left to the contractor. This produces a lower first cost design, but tends to add to the cost of the completed project. The lack of design details also can lead, and frequently does, to a greater number of change orders during construction and to contractor claims at a later date.

For these reasons, bidding for professional services is not recommended.

---

[3] ASCE Policy Statement #304, Qualifications-Based Selection of Professional Engineers, April 12, 1999.

TWO-ENVELOPE SYSTEM

The two-envelope system involves submission of a technical proposal in one envelope and a price proposal in a second envelope. The client then evaluates the technical proposals and selects the best qualified consultant based on that consultant's technical proposal. At this point, the client opens the price proposal submitted in the second envelope by the selected firm and uses it as a basis for negotiation of contractual scope and fees. If a contract is successfully negotiated with the consultant, the second envelopes submitted by the other candidates are returned unopened. If the negotiations fail to reach a successful conclusion, the client terminates negotiation with the first consultant and initiates negotiation with the second ranked firm, opening its second envelope, but keeping the others sealed. The process continues with subsequent candidates, if necessary, until a successful contract is negotiated, at which point all unopened envelopes are returned.

If the client follows this procedure, the net effect is as outlined under the QBS procedure, provided that the client and the best qualified consultant have extensive discussions to reach complete agreement on the scope of services. This allows the client to utilize the knowledge and experience of the consultant in establishing the scope of services. Upon agreement on scope, the price of services should be negotiated to reflect changes from the original scope used for obtaining proposals.

If both envelopes for all candidates are opened at the same time, a bidding process such as discussed in the section on bidding is initiated, with all of the attendant disadvantages. Procedures should be established to provide confirmation that the second envelope is opened only for the successful proposal.

The QBS procedure is still recommended over the two-envelope system. If used as intended, the two-envelope system is similar to the recommended QBS procedure except that the added costs to prepare a comprehensive scope and price discourage some consultants from participating. The costs to prepare a proper price proposal are considerable for the firms not selected, which increases the overall business costs of consulting engineering and, ultimately, the cost to clients.

SUMMARY

Selecting the best qualified firm is one of the most important decisions the client will make in obtaining a quality final project. Qualifications-based selection is recommended for quality results. The selection process as outlined in Figure 1 must include detailed discussions between the client and the selected consultant to define both the project and the engineer's

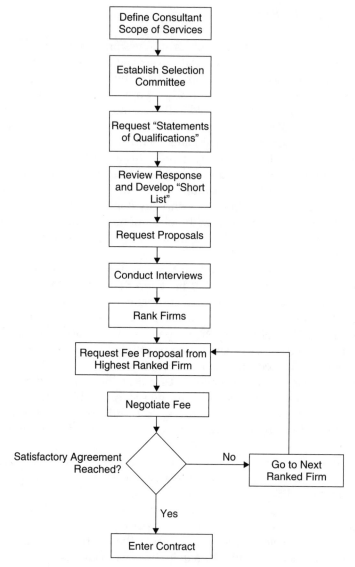

FIGURE 1. *Consultant selection procedure flow chart.*

scope of services. A clear understanding of the contract terms by both parties is essential for a successful project. For additional information regarding the procedure for selecting a consultant, refer to ASCE *Manual No. 73, Quality in the Constructed Project: A Guide for Owners, Designers, and Constructors, Second Edition.*

Chapter 4

METHODS OF CHARGING FOR ENGINEERING SERVICES

Charges for engineering services usually are computed by one of five methods:

1. *Multiplier*—salary cost times multiplier plus direct nonsalary expense
2. *Hourly*—hourly billing rate, plus reimbursables
3. *Per diem*—fixed charge per day
4. *Cost plus fixed fee (CPFF)*
5. *Lump sum*, or fixed price

The first four methods are based on the consultant's costs to perform services. They are referred to as *variable* methods throughout the remainder of this chapter. Variable reimbursement methods are particularly applicable to assignments in which the scope of services is not well defined. The fixed price, or lump sum, method is based on a specific deliverable and requires that the project scope be well defined. Regardless of the payment method employed, the better the scope outlines the expected services, the better the results and the less opportunity for future disagreement between the client and the consultant. Combinations of payment methods for different phases of the contract also can be used. The method or combination of methods used depends on the nature, scope, and complexity of services required by the client. The factors that support the use of one method over the others are summarized in Table 5 at the end of this chapter.

Previous editions of *Manual No. 45* included a percentage of construction cost, or "percentage" method of charging for engineering services; this edition has eliminated the percentage method because it is used infrequently and, more importantly, because of the increasing complexity and large variation in the tasks associated with today's projects.

Many factors will dictate the engineering services required for specific projects. Several are presented in the bulleted list below. The curves included in Chapter 5 show reported fees as a function of construction cost without regard to the chosen payment method. The curves are included for the purpose of estimating engineering costs and should not be used to establish compensation. All of these factors will influence the amount of work required of the consultant and, therefore, will likely cause fees to vary significantly from the specific values predicted by the curves in Chapter 5.

Factors influencing project cost include the following:

- Degree of risk and liability exposure
- Type of client—owner, investor, contractor
- Number of submittals and reviews required by the owner and regulatory agencies
- Number of meetings and presentations made to communities and community groups at the client's request
- Schedule—normal versus accelerated
- Environmental and other regulatory permitting requirements
- Complexity and number of disciplines and subconsultants involved
- Type of construction—new, rehabilitative, or expansion
- Other contract constraints, including the project delivery system— design, build, transfer, operate, or maintain, or combinations of these

To learn more about actual experience with methods of charging for engineering services, ASCE surveyed the practices of consulting firms in 2000. The average percentage of reported use of each of the above methods, in relation to the size of the reporting firm, is listed in Table 1.

As discussed, when the scope of services is uncertain, variable reimbursement methods should be considered. Survey results indicate that frequently these methods are used with a "not-to-exceed" amount. In this case, the client and the consultant should agree beforehand on a method for adjusting the "not-to-exceed" amount when adjustment is warranted. One approach to dealing with uncertainty in the estimate is to include a contingency fee of 5%–10% in the not-to-exceed amount. Another reasonable approach to compensation for uncertain assignments is to require the consultant to inform the client when engineering costs are approaching 75% of a stated budget figure and to update the prior estimate. Such a provision gives the client and the consultant an opportunity to examine progress at that point and, if appropriate, to revise the not-to-exceed amount or the scope of remaining services. The greatest challenge occurs with identifying small changes to scope that by themselves are insignificant but that create a significant change in scope when aggregated.

TABLE 1. Reported Use of Compensation Methods by Consulting Firms. *Consultant's % Use of Each Method During the Previous Year.*

Method of Compensation	Consulting Firm Size[a]		
	Small (1–10)	Medium (11–100)	Large (>100)
Multiplier with not-to-exceed amount	8.9%	14.8%	26.7%
Multiplier without not-to-exceed amount	4.5%	5.2%	6.8%
CPFF with not-to-exceed amount	6.6%	11.1%	15.9%
CPFF without not-to-exceed amount	1.7%	1.6%	2.0%
Lump Sum	32.7%	36.8%	27.9%
Hourly	37.6%	24.6%	12.7%
Other	8.0%	5.9%	8.0%

[a]Number of employees.
Source: 2000 ASCE Survey.

Using the lump sum method, the charge for engineering services is based entirely on the agreed-upon scope of services. This method may be appropriate when the scope of services is well defined and the consultant's costs are within his or her control. A fixed-price method may be used for a complex project by breaking the project into multiple tasks or phases with a fixed price for each task or phase, determined sequentially as the detailed scope of each phase is mutually established.

VALUE PRICING

Occasionally, a consultant has unique qualifications and/or expertise that are not readily available, and/or computer programs that materially decrease the time required for project execution. In some instances, the consultant's proposal might demonstrate that the project can be done easier, faster, safer, or at less cost to achieve the client's objective. Similarly, the client might want the consultant to undertake a project with an accelerated schedule, nonroutine services, or high-risk activities. Under these circumstances, charges for engineering services may be based on "value pricing," which reflects a premium rate not tied directly to the consultant's cost, but rather based on the consultant's unique qualifications or extenuating circumstances. One of the more common value pricing tasks is providing expert witness services.

PAYMENT SCHEDULE

Regardless of the compensation method selected, the agreement should include the provision that payments will be made to the consultant at intervals during the progress of the project. For each of the variable methods, these partial payments should be based on monthly invoices with payment due within a reasonable time after billing or at other stated times. For the fixed-price method, the partial payments should be due at stated intervals—usually once a month—during the performance of the services. These payments may be based on the consultant's statement of percent completion to date or on milestones achieved. Regardless of compensation method and payment schedule, the agreement between the consultant and client also should contain provisions for inflation and delays (see Chapter 6). Agreements for cost-based methods should provide for reimbursement of all direct and indirect project costs, including, but not limited to, those foreseen when the agreement is negotiated. The list of reimbursable items should be as complete and detailed as possible.

ACCOUNTING RECORDS

For services compensated through one of the variable methods, the consultant must provide the accounting records necessary to document and segregate the appropriate expenditures. Detailed hourly time records must be maintained for principals, engineers, and other employees who devote time to the project. Applicable payroll records, together with receipts or other documents to substantiate chargeable expenditures, must be available for audit by the client if required by contract.

COSTS TO PROVIDE ENGINEERING SERVICES

To better understand compensation for engineering services, it is helpful to understand the consultant's costs to provide those services. These costs fall into four general categories: salary cost, payroll burden, other direct costs, and general overhead.

Salary Cost

Salary cost is direct salary and includes salaries for partners or principals and for technical, professional, administrative, and clerical staff directly chargeable to the project.

Payroll Burden

Payroll burden covers all costs associated with employee benefits (nonsalary expenses) and includes the following:

- Sick leave contribution
- Vacation pay
- Holiday pay
- Incentive pay
- Unemployment and other payroll taxes
- Contributions for social security and workers' compensation insurance
- Retirement, medical, and other group benefits

Other Direct Costs

Other direct costs usually incurred in engineering engagements may include the following.

- Living and traveling expenses of principals and employees when away from the home office on business connected to the project.
- Identifiable communications expenses, such as long-distance telephone, facsimile, shipping, and special postage charges for other than general correspondence.
- Expenses for services and equipment directly applicable to the project, such as specialized technical equipment, special legal and accounting services, subconsultants and subcontractors, commercial printing and binding, and similar services that are not applicable for inclusion in general overhead. Many of these services are classified as "special services" and are discussed in more detail in Chapter 2.
- Identifiable drafting supplies, stenographic supplies, and reproduction work (blueprinting, photocopying, and printing) charged to the client's project, as distinguished from such supplies and expenses applicable to several projects.
- Expenses for unusual insurance and specialized health and safety programs and for special clothing for projects with extraordinary risks, such as toxic and hazardous waste conditions.
- Graphic services and audiovisual equipment for public meetings.

General Overhead

The consultant's general overhead is expressed usually as a percentage of salary cost and includes the following indirect costs.

- Provisions for office expenses, including light, heat, telephone, depreciation, rental furniture, rent, drafting equipment and engineering instruments, automobile expenses, and office and drafting supplies not identifiable to a specific project.

- Taxes and insurance other than those included as salary cost, but excluding state and federal income taxes.
- Library and periodical expenses and other costs of keeping abreast of advances in engineering, such as attendance at technical and professional meetings and continuing education courses.
- Executive, administrative, accounting, legal, stenographic, and clerical salaries and expenses (other than identifiable salaries included in salary costs and expenses), plus salaries of partners and principals to the extent that they perform general executive and administrative services, as distinguished from technical or advisory services directly applicable to particular projects. These services and expenses, essential to the conduct of the business, include preliminary arrangements for new projects or assignments and interest on borrowed capital.
- Business development expenses, including salaries of principals and employees so engaged.
- Provision for lost productivity time of technical employees between assignments and for time of principals and employees on public service assignments.
- Costs of acquiring and maintaining computers, developing software, and training staff when not billed as a direct project cost.

The above list of costs is not meant to be comprehensive and gives a general idea of the types of costs in each category. For variable compensation methods, the client will want to reach an agreement with the consultant in advance on the specific costs included in each category.

PROFIT

In addition to salary costs, payroll burden, other direct costs, and general overhead to provide services, the consultant also expects and is entitled to a profit. Profit includes a reasonable margin for contingencies, readiness to serve, knowledge, expertise, and acceptance of risk. Without a reasonable profit, the consultant cannot invest in new technologies and equipment, support the community, allow for business growth, and reward employees. Profit usually is expressed as a percentage of salary cost, payroll burden, and general overhead (see example in Table 2).

SALARY COST TIMES MULTIPLIER PLUS DIRECT NONSALARY EXPENSE

Compensation on the basis of the salary times an agreed multiplier is a frequently used method of determining charges for engineering services.

TABLE 2. Elements of the Consultant's Costs to Provide Service.

Item	Percentage of Salary
1. Salary	100
2. Payroll burden (benefits)	45
3. General overhead	130
4. Total	275
5. Profit (15% × 275)	41
Total with profit	316
6. Other Direct Costs	Actual cost + admin. fee

With this method, charges for engineering services are based primarily on direct salaries. Therefore, the consultant and client should agree on the salary ranges for each applicable classification of service, and on the time period they can be guaranteed. Salary escalation clauses or average salary rates for the anticipated performance period may be employed to help avoid future surprises, misunderstandings, and disputes.

The direct salary times multiplier, or, as it is frequently called, the *direct labor multiplier*, applies a multiplier to unburdened direct labor costs (i.e., direct salaries without employee benefits). The multiplier includes salary cost, payroll burden, general overhead, and profit. In the example shown in Table 2, the multiplier would be 3.16. The size of the multiplier may vary with the type of services, the nature and experience of the consulting firm, size of the firm, and the geographic area in which its office is located. A higher multiplier is applicable typically for services requiring recommendations based on extensive experience and special knowledge, or for services involving expert testimony in legal proceedings. The multiplier may also increase with the experience and special capabilities of the consultant.

The average multiplier applied to the unburdened salary cost for small, medium, and large firms, as reported in the ASCE's 2000 survey, is shown in Table 3.

Table 3 lists the multiplier for the consultant's office staff as well as for staff deployed in the field, such as inspection or resident consultant services during construction.

Other direct costs, item 6 in Table 2, normally are reimbursed by the client at actual invoice cost plus an administration charge to compensate for associated accounting, purchasing, contract administration, risk of liability, etc. Table 3 shows the average percent mark-up for subcontractors and reimbursables as reported in the 2000 survey.

TABLE 3. Multipliers, Mark-Ups, and Fixed Fees.

Size of Firm	Multiplier Office	Multiplier Field	Mark-ups (avg.) %		CPFF Fixed Fee %	
			Subs	Reimbursables	Low	High
Small	2.85	2.58	9.85	9.86	7.72	13.06
Medium	2.87	2.77	7.78	8.19	8.62	13.43
Large	3.21	2.65	7.25	8.00	8.69	15.51
All	2.91	2.61	8.56	8.86	8.30	13.66

Source: 2000 ASCE Survey.

HOURLY BILLING RATE

The hourly billing rate method of compensation is very similar to the salary cost times multiplier method, in that the hourly billing rate includes all direct personnel expenses, overhead, and profit. Other direct costs, as defined under the salary cost times multiplier section, are a separate item for reimbursement—usually with a service charge. Consulting firms may elect to use this method of compensation on projects where the scope of service is not well defined or to simplify accounting and record keeping. Because hourly billing rates vary by region, local rates should be used.

Table 4 presents billing rates for different members of the engineering team, obtained from the results of the 2000 survey. These numbers represent national averages; they may vary greatly by region.

PER DIEM

The term *per diem* refers to the charge for engineering services by classification of employee for a standard day, typically an eight-hour day. Direct personal services of the type described in Chapter 2 are frequently charged on a per-diem basis. This method is particularly well suited to expert witness or similar services and to other short-term engagements involving intermittent personal services.

When per-diem services are furnished, the consultant should be compensated for all of the time devoted, including travel and standby time. The per-diem charge should be based not only on the complexity, risk, and importance of the services, but also on the consultant's professional standing, expertise, and breadth of experience. The consultant also should be reimbursed for travel and subsistence costs and for other out-of-pocket expenses incurred while away from the home office.

For engagements in which the consultant is to appear as an expert, a per-diem charge is considered earned for each day of such appearance. If

TABLE 4. Average Billing Rates by Classification and Size of Firm.

Size of Firm	Avg. $ Principal		Project Manager		Senior Eng		Project Eng		Staff Eng		Land Surveyor		Field Surveyor		Sr. Des Tech		CADD		Draft/Eng Tech		Clerical	
	Low	High	Low	High	Low	High	Low	High	Low	High	Low	High	Low	High	Low	High	Low	High	Low	High	Low	High
Small	98	124	81	98	77	89	65	78	55	66	67	81.3	48.9	62.2	53	65	42	50	39	49	32	38
Medium	113	142	88	110	78	97	68	83	55	69	61	72.3	48.9	61.5	54	67	45	58	40	54	32	44
Large	132	172	97	126	89	113	70	89	56	74	65	83.3	45.4	59.9	55	72	42	60	39	57	34	46
All	108	140	86	108	79	96	67	81	56	69	63	20.3	48.3	61.4	54	67	43	55	39	53	32	42

Source: 2000 ASCE Survey

the consultant is not called to testify or, if called, testifies only part of the day, the full per-diem rate is still charged.

On occasion, the urgency of the engagement can require the consultant's time for periods longer than the normal eight-hour day. In such cases an understanding should be reached with the client, and the per-diem rate increased accordingly.

Per-diem rates vary widely, depending on employee classification, regional location, and period of service. Rates for consultation in connection with litigation and appearances before commissions and courts normally are higher than those charged for other services.

COST PLUS FIXED FEE

Under a cost plus fixed fee agreement, the consultant is reimbursed for the actual costs of all services and supplies related to the project, including the following:

- Salary costs
- General overhead (the consultant should be prepared to support the basis for overhead charges)
- Payroll burden
- Other direct costs
- Fixed fee (profit)

The cost plus fixed fee basis requires, as a prerequisite to equitable negotiations, that the client and the consultant define and agree upon the scope of services to be performed. Such definition of the scope of services is essential to enable the consultant to estimate costs and to propose an equitable fixed fee amount. The scope of services, cost estimate, and fixed fee should be incorporated into the client–consultant agreement.

The cost plus fixed fee method also can be used when the consultant is required to commence services before the detailed scope of services can be determined. In such cases, the following considerations apply.

- The general scale and intent of the project should be fairly well defined, even if the full scope is indeterminate; for example, the number, size, and character of buildings or other facilities; the types of utilities; and other such essential information should be available.
- The types of services to be performed by the consultant should be agreed upon and fully set forth. The agreement also should provide for appropriate adjustments in the fixed fee, in the event that the physical scope of the project, time of completion, or level of effort and services required are materially increased from those contemplated during the negotiations.

The fixed fee amount varies depending on the complexity of the project, uncertainty of the project scope, and other factors that are not a direct function of project size. This amount is frequently calculated as a percentage of the salary costs, overhead, and direct nonsalary expenses. Average fixed fees as a percentage of engineering costs, as reported in the 2000 survey, are shown in Table 3.

LUMP SUM

The lump sum, or fixed price, method of compensation is used frequently for investigations and studies and for basic services on design-type projects where the scope and complexity of the assignment are clearly and fully defined. The fixed price amount can be calculated as the sum total of estimated engineering costs for salaries, overhead and nonsalary expenses, an allowance for contingencies, interest on invested capital, readiness to serve, and a reasonable amount of profit.

A fixed price agreement should contain a clearly stated time period during which the services will be performed and a provision for adjusting compensation if the project is delayed for reasons beyond the consultant's control. For design services, there should be a provision for changes required after approval of the preliminary design, with a clear understanding of where the final approval authority lies.

SUMMARY

A summary of factors relevant to the use of a particular method of compensation is shown in Table 5.

TABLE 5. Summary of Considerations Supporting Each Method of Compensation.

	Reimbursable	Hourly	Per diem	CPFF	Lump Sum
Scope not well defined	▶		▶	▶	▶	
Scope well defined	▶		▶	▶	▶	▶
Simplified accounting					▶
Very short duration assignment		▶	▶		▶
Very complex job	▶				▶	
On-site construction management services		▶	▶		

Chapter 5

TOTAL PROJECT COST

A major concern to a client throughout the planning, design, and construction phases of a project is total construction cost. The total capital cost, often used to establish budgets for a typical project, is composed of the following:

- consultant's costs
- construction costs
- client's costs
- contingency allowance

CONSULTANT'S COSTS

The consultant is often engaged to study and render a planning report on the proposed project, including alternative solutions, layouts, and locations as well as initial estimates of the project cost. These plans may involve alternative or phased implementation, which adds flexibility to the project.

The study and report phase of the construction project may include costs for field or traffic surveys, planning analyses, and geotechnical explorations, in addition to direct engineering costs. In recent years, the impact of governmental rules and regulations on projects has increased dramatically. As a result, so too have the corresponding costs of coordination, evaluation, implementation, and compliance. The extent of these additional cost considerations cannot always be identified during the study and report phase; sometimes they are not quantifiable until after final plans and specifications have been prepared. As a result, clients must understand that the estimated total cost of the project based on the study and report phase is preliminary.

During the final design and construction phases, additional surveying and geotechnical engineering services may be needed. Special or additional engineering services not identified originally may be required by the client or recommended by the consultant. The client also may request that the consultant provide guidance on project start-up or prepare operation and maintenance manuals. In such cases, the appropriate costs should be included in the consultant's compensation. In addition, the consultant must be compensated for any significant changes in the scope of work.

ESTIMATING CONSULTANT'S COSTS

In its 2000 survey of consulting firm practices, ASCE queried members about trends in compensation for engineering services. Consultants were asked to submit data on their completed projects relating the cost of various phases of their engineering services to the construction costs. Data from more than 1,000 projects were submitted and used to compile survey results.

The information was divided into two main categories: new construction and modifications. The projects were also separated by level of complexity—average or above average complexity. The information was then plotted, resulting in two curves on each of four graphs. The graphs show the design fees received versus the construction costs and the total fees received versus construction costs for both new and modification projects. The design fees cover preliminary and final design services only. The total fees cover investigations, studies, preliminary design, final design, construction services, and all other services.

There are limitations to using these graphs to estimate project costs. The scope of work, the complexity of assignments, and the required agency review submittals can vary radically from project to project. Factors such as these have resulted in a decline in the use of the graphs for estimating design fees for consultants over the years. Despite their limitations, the graphs still have value. They can be useful as a general comparison of salary multiplier, hourly cost plus fixed fee, and lump sum methods of compensation. Their traditional acceptance allows them to be used for approximating fees during early project planning. While recognizing their limitations, the client and the consultant can use the graphs during preliminary discussions. Final compensation, however, always should be negotiated after the scope of work has been clearly defined.[4]

---

[4] ASCE conducted this survey of historical information for the benefit of its members and others involved in design and construction. The information in the survey is not a projection of future fees or costs. The survey was conducted in accordance with all applicable laws, including antitrust laws. The survey is limited to information voluntarily and confidentially

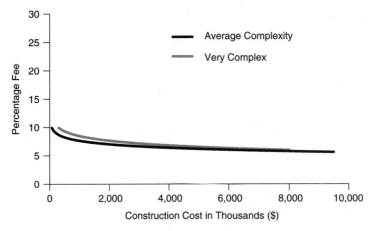

GRAPH 1. *Design Fee vs. Construction Cost for New Construction.*

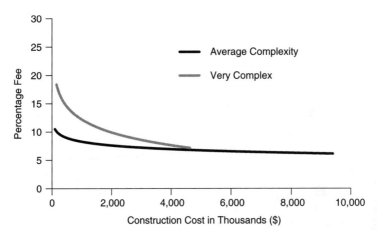

GRAPH 2. *Design Fee vs. Construction Cost for Modifications.*

Graph 1 shows the average design fee versus construction cost for new construction projects. Graph 2 shows the design fee versus construction cost for modification projects. Graph 3 shows the total fee versus construction cost for new construction projects. Graph 4 shows the total fee versus construction cost for modification projects.[5]

---

submitted by survey respondents, and should not be construed as representative of the entire field. ASCE makes no recommendations or suggestions for action regarding the use of the survey results, and all activities and use of information are subject to independent discretion and business judgement.

[5] These curves were generated by fitting a logarithmic curve to the survey data for the prime consultant only using Microsoft Excel.

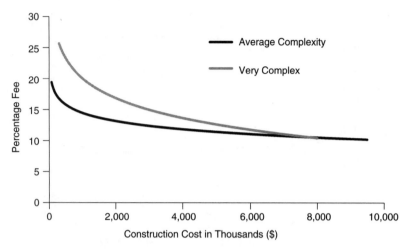

GRAPH 3. *Total Fee vs. Construction Cost for New Construction.*

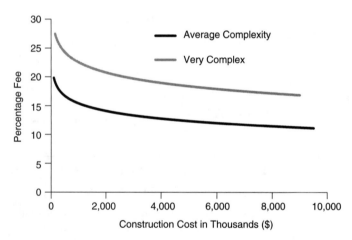

GRAPH 4. *Total Fee vs. Construction Cost for Modifications.*

Any particular project is not likely to lie directly on a curve. The curves represent an average of hundreds of projects of varying complexity. However, these graphs can help in approximating the design fees and total fees for budgeting and comparison purposes.

Because projects vary in nature and scope, no individual historical cost information is provided in this manual for the study and report phase. However, this phase is important because its implementation determines the scope of the entire project and its ultimate capital and life-cycle cost.

CONSTRUCTION COSTS

The study and report phase of the project usually includes a preliminary estimate of the construction costs for the project and alternative approaches. Such cost estimates are approximate, since the final design drawings and specifications have not yet been prepared. In addition, the timing of the construction work must be considered in the estimate because inflation will affect the total construction costs. For this reason, the estimated construction costs at the study and report phase should be related to a recognized cost index. Other conditions being equal, cost estimates can be updated using the cost index if the project construction period is delayed.

One of the best sources of information on national and regional construction cost trends is the Construction Cost Index History published by the *Engineering News Record* (ENR). Using the year 1913 as a base of 100, recent national indices are shown in Table 6.

ENR cautions that the "construction cost indices reflect wage rate and material price trends. They do not adjust for labor, job efficiency, material availability, competitive conditions, management, mechanization, or other intangibles affecting construction costs." Up-to-the-minute information on these cost indices is available on ENR's Web site, *www.enr.com*.

When construction is delayed, significant increases in previous cost estimates may be required. Therefore, all estimates should specify the period for which they are valid. For example, current estimates for projects that will not be built for three years must be modified based on the projected construction schedule. Recent history and current conditions, in

TABLE 6. ENR Construction Cost Index.

Year	Average Index	% Increase from Preceding Year
1991	4835	2.2
1992	4985	3.1
1993	5210	4.5
1994	5408	3.8
1995	5471	1.2
1996	5620	2.7
1997	5825	3.6
1998	5920	1.7
1999	6060	2.4
2000	6222	2.7
2001	6342	1.9

addition to the long-term historical data, should be taken into account in preparing the estimate.

Client's Costs

Client's costs normally include such expenses as legal fees, land costs, administrative costs, staffing costs, and financial costs. These costs and others—including audits, the cost of issuing bonds, and interest on borrowed money during construction—are part of the total project cost and can be estimated best in cooperation with the consultant.

CONTINGENCY ALLOWANCE

Because relatively few projects evolve exactly as planned, the total project cost also must include a contingency fund to pay for unanticipated expenses. By understanding that the consultant's estimate is only that, an estimate, the client will be far less alarmed by unexpected, additional fees and costs. As the project moves forward from the study and report phase through final design and, finally, to construction, more becomes known about project details and costs, and the contingency allowance can then be reduced.

By including a contingency fund, to an extent the unanticipated expenses will fall into the category of "known unknowns." Because they will have been budgeted, they will create less cause for concern.

To provide for these unknowns, contingencies should be added routinely to the basic cost estimate. It is common practice to add 25% or more to the estimated total project cost at the completion of the study and report phase. The amount can be reduced to perhaps 15% at the completion of final design and to 10% when the construction bids become known. Larger or more complex projects may require even higher contingencies.

SUMMARY

Total capital costs for a project include consultant's costs, construction costs, client's costs, and contingency costs. Estimates of total project cost should be revised periodically by the consultant as the design moves forward and as more information becomes known.

Chapter 6

CONTRACTS FOR ENGINEERING SERVICES

The terms of agreement between the consultant and the client should be clearly expressed in a written, legally binding document signed by both parties prior to commencement of services. The following should be included:

- identification of all parties concerned
- scope of required services
- responsibility of each party
- schedule
- terms of payment
- deliverables
- limitation of liability

CONTRACT DOCUMENTS

Standard forms of agreement and related documents that reflect current practice have been developed by ASCE in conjunction with the American Consulting Engineers Council (ACEC) and the National Society of Professional Engineers (NSPE). These professional societies participate in the Engineers' Joint Contract Documents Committee (EJCDC) and recommend the use of the contract documents published by that committee. The EJCDC documents are revised regularly. They can be used verbatim or to confirm the adequacy of other documents. A complete listing of EJCDC documents and how to obtain them is provided in Appendix 1.

At present, many different forms of contract documents are in use. Many clients prefer to customize the language to accommodate their particular laws, regulations and customs, and specific projects. Federal agencies often require the use of their own forms of agreement. For contracts involving federal grant or loan funds, many contractual provisions are mandated by federal laws and policies. Nonfederal public agencies also may require the use of specific contract forms and documents. Private clients may use contractual documents of their own choice. Many consultants use forms of agreement that they have developed based on experience and that define such matters as generally accepted duties and obligations of the contracting parties and legal and liability considerations.

CONTRACTS WITH SUBCONSULTANTS

The basic elements of consulting practice are performed by a prime professional who has overall responsibility for planning and designing a project. In many situations, however, a geotechnical engineer, structural engineer, or other specialist may provide services not furnished by the prime professional. Specialists retained by the prime professional are known as *subconsultants*.

The scope of services provided by a subconsultant varies. Subconsultants may provide, among other things, full design services, investigations and reports in defined areas, or reviews of contract drawings. In any case, their services should be explicitly defined in the terms of the contract.

The subconsultant's contract preferably should be incorporated with the prime professional, but it could be with the client in certain situations. In either case, the relationship between the prime professional and the subconsultant, and the client—and the responsibility of each—must be clearly defined in each contract. When the subconsultant's contract is with the prime professional, the terms of the prime professional's contract with the client should apply to the subconsultant's contract.

PROVISION FOR INFLATION AND DELAYS

Inflation can substantially affect the consultant's cost for performing engineering services as well as the cost of project construction. Inflation must be considered when establishing the terms and payments for consulting services. This is especially important for agreements that will extend over a prolonged period of time and for projects whose initiation or completion are delayed due to factors beyond the consultant's control.

If the consultant's compensation is based on actual costs—e.g., if compensation is based on salary costs times an agreed multiplier plus direct nonsalary expenses, or on a cost plus fixed fee basis—then any increase in the cost of engineering services due to delays is automatically accommodated.

This automatic adjustment does not occur when compensation is based on specified hourly or per-diem rates, a fixed-price contract, a salary cost times multiplier, or a cost plus fixed-fee contract for which maximum compensation has been established. In such cases, additional contract provisions are required. For example:

- Agreements using specified hourly or per-diem rates, or specifying a maximum allowable compensation, should stipulate the time period for which the rates will remain in effect, after which appropriate adjustments can be made for inflation.
- Fixed-price contracts should be negotiated on the basis of a suitable project period, with provision for appropriate adjustment in compensation if the period is exceeded because of factors beyond the consultant's control. Whenever a maximum fee is stipulated, changes in scope necessitate an adjustment in the upset figure, regardless of the type of contract.

DOCUMENT OWNERSHIP

All documents, including drawings, computations, and specifications prepared or furnished by a consultant, are instruments of service with respect to the specific project under contract. The consultant should retain an ownership and property interest in these documents whether or not the project is completed, unless otherwise stipulated in the contract documents. Normally, the client will make and retain copies for information and reference in connection with the use and occupancy of the project. However, the documents are not intended for reuse on extensions of the project or for any other project without written verification or adaptation by the consultant. The contract should provide that the consultant is held harmless and indemnified by the client should there be any reuse of the documents for other projects or extensions without the consultant's written permission.

An increasing number of clients are mandating that electronic documentation be provided by the consultant as part of the contract deliverables. The ownership and reuse of certain portions of these electronic files should remain with the consultant.

Electronic documents should be secured; the file identity of the author or originating firm can be easily deleted or altered, leaving the origin of the computer file or document in doubt. Therefore, much like manually drafted documents, electronic deliverables should be copyrighted by the consultant to limit their legal use and modifications. Whenever sharing of computer-generated documents occurs, the contractual agreement between parties should specify, in detail, the intended use of any electronic deliverable. Appropriate disclaimers and warnings for any expressed use of the data should be clearly identified.

ALTERNATIVE DISPUTE RESOLUTION

Alternative dispute resolution (ADR) is being used more frequently in the construction industry to avoid the formal and more costly litigation route through the courts. Currently used ADR procedures include both binding and nonbinding methods such as mediation, arbitration, private judging, and dispute review boards. No single method is best for all situations. The method to be used should be determined at the beginning of the project.

ADR relies on the premise that disputes arise because of differences of opinion on technical issues. Therefore, disputes should be resolved on the basis of nonbiased professionals deciding the dispute using their technical expertise. Many ADR methods rely on the conciliatory approach to resolution. Lawsuits are an opposite approach. They immediately set up adversarial positions that usually polarize the disputants. Emotions rather than logic tend to dominate the negotiations. Ultimately, judges or juries, who possess little or no technical expertise on the issues, may resolve the dispute. The use of conciliatory ADR will often facilitate the following:

- quicker resolution;
- lower-cost resolution; and
- nonadversarial proceedings.

As a result, ADR often allows the disputants to maintain a good working relationship after the dispute is resolved.

The EJCDC has recommended dispute resolution provisions in both its "Standard Form of Agreement Between Owner and Engineer for Professional Services" (E-500, Section 6.09) and "Standard General Conditions of the Construction Contract" (C-700, Section 16). The provisions potentially involve a two-step procedure, first requiring nonbinding mediation, followed, if necessary, by binding arbitration.

Provisions for dispute resolution should be included in the contract, preferably using a conciliatory rather than an adversarial method.

STANDARD OF CARE

Agreements should state that the consultant will strive to perform services in a manner consistent with the level of care and skill ordinarily exercised by members of the engineering profession practicing under similar circumstances in the locality of the project. Also, consultants should be responsible only for their own negligent acts, errors, and omissions.

RETAINAGE

Some clients include provisions for retaining a portion of the consultant's compensation until completion of the project. Unfortunately, retainage results in a financial burden for the consultant and higher overhead costs that must be passed on to subsequent clients. It is recommended that agreements for engineering services exclude a retainage provision. However, if a governmental or other administrative code requires retainage, it is recommended that the agreement specify a reasonable maximum amount to be retained. It also should provide that the retained funds earn interest in favor of the consultant, and provide for release of the funds after an agreed time period, especially when the project completion or other time period has been extended for reasons beyond the control of the consultant. The agreement should further provide for a gradual reduction in the percentage of fee retained consistent with the percentage completion of the project.

PARTNERING

Partnering is an old concept receiving renewed emphasis in the construction industry. It is mandated by some agencies, and strongly supported by major players in all three segments of the building industry—owners, contractors, and designers.

Partnering is a relationship among shareholders in a project—the owner, the designer, and the builder—in which they recognize and acknowledge their common goals and potential risks. Contracts establish the legal relationships among shareholders while partnering establishes the working relationships. Partnering is built on trust, commitment, and equity. It requires a formal agreement on jointly developed mutual goals and project objectives. It requires prompt resolution of problems at the lowest level of authority. ASCE encourages partnering in construction contracts. For additional information on partnering, see *Manual No. 73, Quality in the Constructed Project, Second Edition.*

TERMINATION

Since there is always the possibility that a project could be terminated for a variety of reasons, the right of either party to terminate the contract prior to its completion, as well as the terms under which the agreement can be terminated, should be clearly stated in the contract. In the event of termination, the consultant should be compensated fully for the work performed. Estimated completion may be greater than shown on routine reports to the client based on preliminary work completed but not yet shown on the contract documents.

An agreed-upon settlement figure should be based on the following:

- Work completed as per most recent project report;
- Preliminary work done but not yet included on contract documents or on progress reports;
- Organization of all completed and partially completed work;
- Demobilization, including filing of all documents so that quick startup can be done if the project is reinstated;
- Time and cost required to assess work completed and negotiate settlement with client;
- Release of retainage.

Cooperation by both the client and the consultant is absolutely necessary for a satisfactory resolution of the final compensation due the consultant.

PERFORMANCE EVALUATION

Upon project completion, it is recommended that the client evaluate the consultant's performance. Two or three people from the client's staff should independently complete the evaluation form, which should include the following questions at a minimum:

- Did the consultant complete the project on time and within budget?
- Were the consultant's services satisfactory?
- Did the consultant relate satisfactorily to the client and contractors?
- Did the consultant coordinate the services of subconsultants and/or subcontractors satisfactorily?
- Were the services accurate and complete?
- Was the consultant's staff competent and professional?
- Did the consultant properly represent the client at public meetings and other dealings with the general public?
- Would the client retain the consultant on a future project?

After the client completes the evaluation form, it should be furnished to the consultant and a meeting should be scheduled to discuss the evaluation. The client and consultant should be candid in discussing the evaluation and reach an understanding on the reasons for the performance. The client also might want to evaluate its own performance to the consultant. Both the client and the consultant should sign the evaluation.

SUMMARY

The elements of the contract for engineering services must be carefully written and thoroughly reviewed by both parties prior to signature. A clear understanding of each party's duties and responsibilities will avoid problems during the development of project documents.

For additional information on this subject, refer to ASCE *Manual No. 73, Quality in the Constructed Project: A Guide for Owners, Designers, and Constructors, Second Edition*, Chapter 7.

APPENDIX 1

EJCDC DOCUMENTS[6]

E-564	Agreement Between Engineer and Geotechnical Engineer [1996]
E-568	Standard Form of Agreement Between Engineer and Architect [1996]
E-570	Standard Form of Agreement Between Engineer and Consultant [1999]
E-571	Amendment to Engineer-Consultant Agreement [1999]
1910-82	Engineer-Subconsultant Agreements: Combined Offer; E-564, E-568 & E-570 (hard copy binder)
E-820-P	Engineer-Subconsultant Agreements: Combined Offer; E-564, E-568 & E-570 (hard copy binder plus WordPerfect 5.1 disk)
E-820-M	Engineer-Subconsultant Agreements: Combined Offer; E-564, E-568 & E-570 (hard copy binder plus MS Word disk)
E-001	Owner-Engineer Agreement, General Instructions [1996]
E-500	Agreement Between Owner and Engineer (Full Services) [1996]
E-501	Amendment to Owner-Engineer Agreement [1999]
E-505	Standard Form of Master Agreement Between Owner and Engineer for Professional Services [1999]

---

[6]Engineers' Joint Contract Documents Committee. Issued and published jointly by: Professional Engineers in Private Practice, a practice division of the National Society of Professional Engineers; American Consulting Engineers Council; and American Society of Civil Engineers.

E-510	Standard Form of Agreement Between Owner and Engineer, Funding Agency Edition [1997]
E-525	Standard Form of Agreement Between Owner and Engineer for Study and Report Phase [1996]
E-530	Standard Form of Agreement Between Owner and Geotechnical Engineer [1996]
E-580	Standard Form of Joint Venture Agreement Between Engineers [1999]
E-581	Standard Form of Agreement Between Owner, Designer, and Project Peer Reviewers for an Independent Project Peer Review [1999]
E-582	Agreement Between Owner & Engineer for Program Management Services [2000]
N-114	Limitation of Liability in Design Professional Contracts [1999]
1910-81	Owner-Engineer Agreements: Combined Offer; E-500, E-525, E-530 (hard copy binder)
1910-81-A	Owner-Engineer Agreements: Combined Offer; E-500, E-525, E-530 (hard copy plus WordPerfect 5.1 disk)
1910-81-B	Owner-Engineer Agreements: Combined Offer; E-500, E-525, E-530 (hard copy plus MS Word 6.0 disk)
1910-83	Funding Agency Editions: Combined Offer; E-510, C-521 & C-710 (hard copy binder)
1910-83-A	Funding Agency Editions: Combined Offer; E-510, C-521 & C-710 (hard copy plus WordPerfect 5.1 disk)
1910-83-B	Funding Agency Editions: Combined Offer; E-510, C-521 & C-710 (hard copy plus MS Word 6.0 disk)
1910-30	Coordinated Multiprime Design Agreement Between Owner and Design Professional for Construction Projects; includes Guide Sheet and Exhibits [1993]
1910-30-A	Guide Sheet—Multiprime Design Agreement [1993]
1910-30-B	Exhibits with Instructions—Multiprime Design Agreement [1993]
P-001	Commentary on Procurement Documents [2000]
P-200	Suggested Instructions to Bidders for Procurement Contracts [2000]
P-400	Suggested Bid Form for Procurement Contracts

P-520	Suggested Form of Agreement Between Buyer and Seller for Procurement Contracts [2000]
P-610	Suggested Performance Bond for Procurement Contracts [2000]
P-615	Payment Bond for Procurement Contracts [2000]
P-700	Standard General Conditions for Procurement Contracts [2000]
P-800	Guide to the Preparation of Procurement Supplementary Conditions [2000]
D-001	Guide to Use of EJCDC Design/Build Documents [2000]
D-500	Standard Form of Agreement Between Owner and Owner's Consultant for Design Professional Services on Design/Build Projects [2000]
D-505	Standard Form of Subagreement Between Design/Builder and Engineer or Design Professional Services [2000]
D-520	Standard Form of Agreement Between Owner and Design/Builder on the Basis of a Stipulated Price [2000]
D-521	Standard Form of Construction Subagreement Between Design/Builder and Subcontractor on the Basis of a Stipulated Price [2000]
D-525	Standard Form of Agreement Between Owner and Design/Builder on the Basis of Cost Plus [2000]
D-526	Standard Form of Construction Subagreement Between Design/Builder and Subcontractor on the Basis of Cost Plus [2000]
D-700	Standard General Conditions of the Contract Between Owner and Design/Builder [2000]
D-750	Standard General Conditions of the Construction Subagreement Between Design/Builder and Subcontractor [2000]
1910-49	Design/Build Documents: Combined Offer; D-001, D-500, D-505, D-521, D-525, D-526, D-700 & D-750 (hard copy binder)
A-490-B	Design/Build Documents: Combined Offer; D-001, D-500, D-505, D-521, D-525, D-526, D-700 & D-750 (hard copy plus WordPerfect 5.1 disk)
A-490-E	Design/Build Documents: Combined Offer; D-001, D-500, D-505, D-521, D-525, D-526, D-700 & D-750 (hard copy plus MS Word 6.0 disk)

A-490-F	Design/Build Documents: Combined Offer; D-001, D-500, D-505, D-521, D-525, D-526, D-700 & D-750 (hard copy plus MS Word for Macintosh disk)
A-490-C	Design/Build Documents: Combined Offer; D-001, D-500, D-505, D-521, D-525, D-526, D-700 & D-750 (hard copy plus WordPerfect for Macintosh disk)
A-490-A	Design/Build Documents: Combined Offer; D-001, D-500, D-505, D-521, D-525, D-526, D-700 & D-750 (hard copy plus WordPerfect for DOS disk)
C-001	Construction Documents, General & Instructions [2001]
C-050	Owner's Instructions Regarding Bidding Procedures and Construction Contract Documents [2001]
C-051	Engineer's Letter to Owner Requesting Instructions Concerning Bonds and Insurance for Construction [2001]
C-052	Owner's Instructions to Engineer Concerning Bonds and Insurance for Construction [2001]
C-200	Guide to the Preparation of Instruction to Bidders [2001]
C-400	Guide to the Preparation of Bid Form [2001]
C-430	Bid Bond, Penal Sum Form [2001]
C-435	Bid Bond, Damages Form [2001]
C-510	Notice of Award [2001]
C-520	Standard Form of Agreement Between Owner and Contractor on the Basis of a Stipulated Price [2001]
C-521	Standard Form of Agreement Between Owner and Contractor on the Basis of a Stipulated Price, Funding Agency Edition [2001]
C-525	Standard Form of Agreement Between Owner and Contractor on the Basis of Cost-Plus [2001]
C-550	Notice to Proceed [2001]
C-610	Construction Performance Bond [2001]
C-615	Construction Payment Bond [2001]
C-620	Application for Payment [2001]
C-625	Certificate of Substantial Completion [2001]
C-700	Standard General Conditions of the Construction Contract [2001]

C-710	Standard General Conditions of the Construction Contract, Funding Agency Edition [2001]
C-800	Guide to the Preparation of Supplementary Conditions [2001]
C-940	Work Change Directive [2001]
C-941	Change Order [2001]
1910-84	Construction Documents: Combined Offer; 19 Construction-Related Documents (hard copy)
C-990-P	Construction Documents: Combined Offer; 19 Construction-Related Documents (hard copy plus WordPerfect 5.1 disk)
C-990-M	Construction Documents: Combined Offer; 19 Construction-Related Documents (hard copy plus MS Word disk)
N-103	Summary of Changes to Construction Related Documents [1997]
N-117	Focus on Shop Drawings [2001]
N-119	Recommended Competitive Bidding Procedures for Construction Projects [2001]
R-001	Guide and Commentary on Remediation Documents [2000]
R-520	Standard Form of Agreement Between Owner and Environmental Remediator on the Basis of Stipulated Price [2000]
R-521	Standard Form of Construction Agreement Between Environmental Remediator and Subcontractor on the Basis of a Stipulated Price [2000]
R-525	Standard Form of Agreement Between Owner and Environmental Remediator and Subcontractor on the Basis of Cost-Plus [2000]
R-526	Standard Form of Construction Subagreement Between Environmental Remediator and Subcontractor on the Basis of Cost-Plus [2000]
R-700	Standard General Conditions of the Contract Between Owner and Environmental Remediator [2000]
R-750	Standard General Conditions of the Construction Subagreement Between Environmental Remediator and Subcontractor [2000]
N-101	Commentary on Agreements for Engineering Services and Construction-Related Documents [2000]

N-104	Other Engineering Agreements [2000]
N-110	Engineer Status During Construction [2000]
N-111	Dispute Resolution [1998]
N-112	Indemnification by Engineers—A Warning [1999]
N-113	Insurance/Bonds
N-115	Ownership of Documents [1999]
N-116	Safety [2000]
N-118	Payment to Contractor [1999]
N-120	Advice 97 AIA [1999]
N-121	Joint Venture Agreement [2000]
1910-16	Uniform Location of Subject Matter [2000]

APPENDIX 2
ENGINEER SELECTION
PROCESS—TYPICAL FORMS

Statement of Qualifications Evaluation Form
Statement of Qualifications Evaluation Summary Form
Reference Check Form
Letter to Consultants Not Selected for an Interview
Letter to Short Listed Consultants
Interview Process Score Sheet

Statement of Qualifications Evaluation Form

Evaluator:
. . . .
Project Identification:
. . . .
Consultant:
. . . .
Address:
. . . .
City/State/ZIP:
. . . .
Telephone: Contact:
. . . .

	Rating (1–5)*	Weight (1–10)**	Total
1. Firm's history and resource capability to perform required services	____ ×	____ =	____
2. Related consultant experiences	____ ×	____ =	____
3. Experience of program manager	____ ×	____ =	____
4. Qualifications of assigned personnel	____ ×	____ =	____
5. Ability to meet schedule	____ ×	____ =	____
6. Ability to meet project budget	____ ×	____ =	____
7. Approach to quality assurance/control	____ ×	____ =	____
8. Reference check	____ ×	____ =	____
		Grand Total	____

*Rate firms from 1 to 5 with 1 being least favorable and 5 most favorable.
** Weight factors from 1 to 10 with 1 being least important and 10 most important.
Note: Additional items should be added to meet the specific project requirements.

Statements of Qualifications Evaluation Summary Form

Client:
. . . .

Project Identification:
. . . .

Enter each reviewer's grand total for each firm from the Statement of Qualifications Evaluation Form.

	Consultants									
	1	**2**	**3**	**4**	**5**	**6**	**7**	**8**	**9**	**10**
Reviewer 1										
Reviewer 2										
Reviewer 3										
Reviewer 4										
Reviewer 5										
Reviewer 6										
Total										

Select the three highest rated firms for future consideration.

Reference Check Form

Client:
. . . .
Project Identification:
. . . .
Consultant:
. . . .

Reference Information:
. . . .
Client:
. . . .
Address:
. . . .
Referred Project:
. . . .
Contact Person:
. . . .

1. When was project completed?

2. Did the consultant listed above do the work?

3. Describe the services provided by the consultant.

4. Who was the staff person assigned to work with you on this project? How satisfied were you with this person?

5. Was the project started on schedule?

6. Was the project completed as planned?

7. Were the budget, cost control, and financial administration within the planned controls and limitations?

8. Did the consultant and you (the client) work well as a team?

9. Did the consultant work well with other committees and public agencies?

10. How would you rate the consultant's performance on a scale of 1 to 5 with 1 being the least favorable and 5 being the most favorable?

Letter to Consultants Not Selected for an Interview

Re: Request for Statement of Qualifications

Dear   :

The committee would like to express its appreciation to your firm for submitting your statement of qualifications for providing professional services for the proposed project.

After careful consideration of all firms submitting qualifications, the committee has made a decision to interview three firms.

For your information, the firms selected for further consideration are:
1.
2.
3.

We hope that your firm will continue to participation in our selection process for future projects.

Sincerely yours,

(The Committee Chairman)

Letter to Short Listed Consultants

Re: (Project Identification)

Dear   :

The selection committee has selected your firm for further consideration to provide professional services for the referred project. An interview with your firm will be held (day, date, time) at (location).

To assist you in preparing your presentation, the following items are attached:
- Copies of material relevant to the project
- Copy of the interview score sheet that will be used by the selection committee
- (Other items)

You will be allowed 30 minutes for your presentation and 30 minutes to answer questions posed by the committee. Your project manager should be present at the interview and play a major role in your presentation.

Following completion of the interview with the other short listed firms, the committee will rank the firm in accordance with the attached score sheet. The highest ranked firm will then be requested to submit a cost proposal for the service and to negotiate a contract. If contract terms cannot be reached, the second ranked firm will be contacted.

For your information, the other short listed firms are:
1.
2.
3.

The selection committee looks forward to hearing your presentation and appreciates your interest in providing professional service to our agency.

Sincerely,

(Selection Committee Chair)

Interview Process Score Sheet

Evaluator:
. . . .

Identification:
. . . .

Categories	Rating		Weight		Total
1. Related project experience	_____	×	_____	=	_____
2. Firm's ability and capacity to perform the work	_____	×	_____	=	_____
3. Key personnel assigned to the project	_____	×	_____	=	_____
4. Consultant approach to satisfy project requests	_____	×	_____	=	_____
5. Project manager experience	_____	×	_____	=	_____
6. Management approach for cost control	_____	×	_____	=	_____
7. Proposed schedule	_____	×	_____	=	_____
8. Quality control program	_____	×	_____	=	_____
9. Outside consultants needed	_____	×	_____	=	_____
			Grand Total		_____

Note: Additional items should be added to meet specific project requirements.

GLOSSARY

A

Addenda—Written or graphic instruments issued prior to the opening of bids that clarify, correct, or change the bidding requirements or the contract documents.

Additional Services—Services to be performed for or furnished to owner by engineer.

Agreement—Mutual understanding between two or more parties creating obligation between competent parties who enter engagement with each other by a promise on either side

Alternative Dispute Resolution (ADR)—The practice of involving non-biased professionals using their technical expertise to resolve disputes.

Appraisal—Valuation of property by the estimate of an authorized person.

Arbitration—Hearing and determination of a case in controversy, by a person chosen by the parties or appointed under statutory authority.

B

Bid—Complete and properly signed proposal to perform construction required by contract documents, or designated portion of the documents, for an amount or amounts stipulated in the documents. A bid is submitted in accordance with bidding documents.

Bidding Documents—Advertisement or invitation to bid, instructions to bidders, the bid form, and the proposed contract documents (including all addenda issued prior to receipt of bids).

C

CADD—Acronym for Computer Aided Design and Drafting, an engineering application used to produce computer-generated designs.

Change Order—Written order to the constructor signed by the owner and/or by the owner's agent or representative, issued after execution of a contract, authorizing a change in the work or an adjustment in the contract sum or the contract time.

Client—Person or organization by whom an engineer or architect is employed, to whom they are responsible and from whom they draw fees; usually the building owner in a building contract.

Codes—Regulations, ordinances, or statutory requirements of, or meant for adoption by, governmental units relating to building construction and occupancy, adopted and administered for the protection of the public health, safety, and welfare.

Code of Ethics—Official statements prepared by organizations representing members of a profession that establish fundamental principles, canons, and guidelines of practice for the members of that profession.

Compensation—Payment for services, especially wages or remuneration.

Construction Cost—Total cost to the client for the execution of the work authorized at one time and handled in each separate phase of engineering services, excluding fees or other costs for engineering and legal services, the cost of land, rights-of-way, legal and administrative expenses, but including the direct costs to the client of all final construction contracts; and including all items of construction (including labor, materials, and equipment) required for the completed work (including extras) and the total value at project site of all labor, materials, and equipment for the project.

Construction Manager—Prime professional on the job site; may be either the constructor or a member of the constructor's staff.

Constructor—Professional responsible for planning, managing, and accomplishing the construction necessary to build the project in accordance with contract documents.

Consultant—Person or entity who provides specialized advice or services to an owner, design professional, or constructor.

Consulting Engineer (qualified individual or firm)—Chartered civil or structural engineer who is engaged by an architect or client or another engineer for the purpose of designing a structure. The engineer advises the client on the choice of structure. Once the structure is chosen, the engineer ceases to advise and begins to draw out a structural scheme, expanding it in detail after the client's approval.

Contingency Allowance—Percentage added to the basic cost estimate to allow for unknown costs.

Contingency Basis—Means of providing professional services at reduced cost in expectation of favorable consideration for future projects.

Contract Documents—Owner/constructor agreement, the conditions of the contract (general, supplementary, and other conditions), drawings, specifications, and all addenda issued prior to and all modifications issued after execution of the contract, and any other items that may be specifically stipulated as being included.

Contractor—Person or entity with whom owner enters into a written agreement covering construction work to be performed or furnished with respect to the project.

Cost Plus Fixed Fee (CPFF)—Payment agreement in which the consulting engineer is reimbursed for the actual costs of all services and supplies related to the project.

D

Design-Build—Construction contract delivery method in which the client has design prepared to a concept stage and then allows a contractor to bid for the work at that stage. The contractor with a design partner will complete the design and construct the project. This delivery method does not necessarily save money, but can save time if the client is willing to give up some control of the process. The contractor also is given some flexibility over the details under this approach.

Design-Build-Operate-Maintain (DBOM)—Similar to design-build except that in addition to designing and constructing, the contractor team operates and maintains the project for an agreed period of time. Used for toll roads and transit projects where the contract collects the revenues to pay for part or all of the construction and operations costs and then turns the completed project over to the client at some point in the future, for example thirty-five years.

Design Competition—Process through which a consultant is selected above other competitors based on proposal of an innovative approach to solving a client's needs.

Direct Costs—Direct costs are the consultant's costs, excluding salaries and benefits, that can be directly attributed to a specific project, for example, travel, subconsultant expenses, etc.

Direct Nonsalary Expense—Living and traveling expenses of principals and employees when away from the home or office on business connected with the project; identifiable communications expenses, such as long-distance telephone, telegraph, cable, shipping and special postage charges other than general correspondence; expenses for services and equipment directly applicable to the work; expenses for unusual insurance; project professional liability insurance.

Direct Salary Cost—Earnings plus fringe benefits for partners, principals, and all technical, professional, administrative, and clerical staff directly chargeable to the project, including sick leave, vacation, holiday and incentive pay, unemployment and other payroll taxes, social security, worker's compensation, retirement, and medical and other group benefits.

E

Engineer of Record—Prime professional engineer or organization legally responsible for the engineering design.

Expert Witness—Nonbiased professional who provides testimony based upon his/her technical expertise.

F

Feasibility Study— (1) Study of applicability or desirability of any management or procedural system from the standpoint of advantages versus disadvantages in any given case; (2) study to determine the time at which it would be practicable or desirable to install such a system when determined to be advantageous; or (3) study to determine whether a plan is capable of being accomplished successfully.

Firm—Business unit or enterprise.

H

Hourly Billing Rate—Method of payment in which all direct personnel expenses, overhead, and profit are charged to the client at a determined cost per hour.

I

Instruction to Bidders—Directions contained in the bidding documents for preparing and submitting bids for a construction project or designated portion of a project.

L

Level of Effort Contract—Contract procedure used to supplement a client's staff, either by providing an extension to existing disciplines and capabilities already on board or by adding special disciplines not available on the client's staff.

Life-Cycle Cost—Total cost of developing, owning, operating, and maintaining a constructed project for its economic life, including its fuel and energy costs.

Lump Sum—Single price bid determined and submitted by the engineer for a completed facility, which includes costs for materials and work hours. The lump sum amount can be calculated as the sum total of estimated engineering costs for salaries, overhead, and nonsalary expenses, an allowance for contingencies, interest on invested capital, readiness to serve, and a reasonable amount for profit. Lump sum compensation for basic services on certain design-type projects can also be computed as an appropriate percentage of estimated construction costs.

M

Median—A value in an ordered set of values below and above which there is an equal number of values, or which is the arithmetic mean of the two middle values if there is no one middle number.
Mediation—Intervention between conflicting parties to promote reconciliation, settlement, or compromise.
Multiplier—Factor applied to the salary cost to compensate the consulting engineer for overhead expenses, contingencies, interest on invested capital, readiness to serve, and profit.

N

Negotiation—Action or process of conferring with another so as to arrive at the settlement of some matter.

O

Overhead—Business expenses (such as rent, heat, or insurance) not chargeable to a particular part of the work or product.
Owner—Individual or group that initiates a construction project and is responsible for financing the project.

P

Partnering—Working relationship among the stakeholders in a project—the owner, designer, and the builder—in which they recognize and acknowledge their common goals and potential risks.
Payroll Burden—Payroll burden refers to all costs associated with employee benefits and is typically expressed as a percentage of salary cost.
Peer Review—Structured, independent review of an organization or project by a team of experts who are completely external to the subject under review, and with at least the same level of expertise and experience as those responsible for the project or practice.
Per-Diem—Daily allowance or fee, normally based on an eight-hour day.
Prime Consultant (prime professional)—Design professional who has the overall responsibility for planning and designing a project.
Profit—Profit is the return received by the consultant on a project after all operating expenses have been met and includes a reasonable margin for

contingencies, readiness to serve, knowledge, expertise, and acceptance of risk.

Project—Total construction as defined by the contract documents.

Project Management—Contract delivery method typically used on large complex projects in which a consultant is hired to coordinate all the activities necessary to complete a project. This could include bidding out the construction to a number of contractors and consultants and coordinating their results to provide the client with a completed package.

Q

Qualifications-Based Selection (QBS)—Method of choosing a design professional based upon criteria of skills, experience, and expertise, rather than cost.

R

Reimbursables—Expenses incurred directly in connection with the performance or furnishing of basic and additional services for the project for which owner shall pay engineer.

Rent-a-Judge—Method of dispute resolution contemplated by specific state statutes permitting the trial of certain types of civil cases by an individual whose decision carries the weight of a trial court decision and is appealable as a trial court decision would be. Also referred to as "private judging."

Request for Proposal (RFP)—Petition to seek consultants for creating a "short list" of qualified consulting engineers for purpose of selecting one for a specific project.

Request for Qualifications (RFQ)—Petition to determine the eligibility of a selected design professional in a specific area of expertise.

Resident Project Representative (RPR)—The individual representing the owner, sometimes selected from the design professional's firm, who administers the construction contract and monitors progress and relationships among project site personnel.

Retainage—Sum withheld from progress payments to the design professional or constructor, according to terms of owner/designer or owner/constructor agreements, until completion of the project.

S

Salary Cost— Salary cost is the direct salary cost of personnel excluding benefits.

Scope of Services—Definition of the project requirements.

Specifications—Those portions of the contract documents consisting of written technical descriptions of materials, equipment, construction systems, standards, and workmanship as applied to the work, and all applicable administrative details.

Start-up—Preparing the project or facility for occupancy or use and testing the systems in that facility for operation.

Statement of Qualifications—Form or brochure that contains the credentials of a design professional.

Stipend—Fixed sum of money paid for services.

Subconsultant—Person or organization that has a direct contract with the design professional.

Subcontractor—Person or organization that has a direct contract with the constructor.

Supplier—Manufacturer, fabricator, distributor, material supplier, or vendor having a direct contract with contractor or with any subcontractor to furnish materials or equipment to be incorporated in the work by contractor or subcontractor.

T

Turnkey—See **Design-Build.**

Two-Envelope System—Method of selecting a design professional in which the technical proposal is submitted in one envelope and the price proposal in a second.

V

Value Engineering—Organized approach to identify efficiently costs that do not contribute measurably to a project's quality, utility, durability, or appearance, or to the owner's requirements.

Value Pricing—Value pricing is a method of establishing a consultant's reimbursement based upon the relative value of the product provided rather than the consultant's cost to provide the product. Quite often value pricing reflects a premium rate based upon the consultant's unique qualifications or extenuating circumstances.

REFERENCES

A *Dictionary of Civil Engineering* by John Scott, made and printed in Great Britain, copyright 1958

McGraw-Hill Dictionary of Engineering, copyright 1984

Dictionary of Civil Engineering by Rolt Hammond, Great Britain 1965

INDEX

accounting records 32
ACEC (American Consulting Engineers Council) 47
ADR (alternative dispute resolution) 50
adversarial dispute resolution 50
alternative dispute resolution (ADR) 50
American Bar Association's Model Procurement Code for State and Local Governments 6
American Consulting Engineers Council (ACEC) 47
appraisals, valuations, and rate studies 10
Architect-Engineer and Related Services Questionnaire (Form SF 254) 20–21, 24
Architect-Engineer and Related Services Questionnaire for Specific Projects (Form SF 255) 22, 24
ASCE: contract development 47
ASCE Code of Ethics 6–7
associate consultants 9

bidding 25–26; compared to two-envelope system 27
bidding phase 12, 14
billing rate, hourly 36, 37 (table), 48–49
Brooks Act 6
budget 3–4

charging methods 29–39, 31 (table), 39 (table); accounting records 32; cost plus fixed fee (CPFF) 38–39; costs of engineering services 32–34, 35 (table); factors influencing project cost 30–31; hourly billing rate 36, 37 (table);

lump sum 31, 32, 39; multiplier method 34–35, 36 (table); payment schedule 32; percentage of construction cost 29; per diem 36, 38; profit 34; value pricing 31
client-consultant relationships 2–3
client's costs 46
compensation 23–24
conciliatory dispute resolution 50
Construction Cost Index History (ENR) 45, 45 (table)
construction costs 45–46, 45 (table); vs design fee for modifications 43 (graph); vs design fee for new construction 43 (graph); vs total fee for modifications 44 (graph); vs total fee for new construction 44 (graph)
construction phase 12, 14–15
construction projects 11–15
consultant's costs 41–42; estimating 42–44, 43 (graph), 44 (graph)
consultations, investigations, and studies 10–11
consulting engineer selection 5–6, 19–28; basis for selection 19–20; bidding 25–26, 27; open-end contract procedure 25; procedure flow chart 28 (figure); qualifications-based selection (QBS) procedure 21–24, 25, 27; selection committee 20; Statement of Qualifications file 20–21; suggestions 24–25
contingency allowance 46
contingency basis of employment 6–7
contracts 9, 47–53; alternative dispute resolution (ADR) 50; document ownership 49; documents 47–48;

partnering   51; performance
   evaluation   52; provision for
   inflation and delays   48–49;
   qualifications-based selection
   (QBS) procedure   24, 25;
   retainage   51; standard of care
   50; with subconsultants   48;
   termination   51–52
cost, total project. See total project cost
cost plus fixed fee (CPFF)   38–39,
   48–49
costs, client's   46
costs, construction. See construction
   costs
costs, consultant's. See consultant's
   costs
costs of engineering services   32–34,
   35 (table); general overhead
   33–34; other direct costs   33;
   payroll burden   33; salary cost
   32; secondary to qualifications
   26
CPFF (cost plus fixed fee)   38–39,
   48–49

DBOM (design-build-operate-and-
   maintain)   2–3,
   4–5
delays, provision for   48–49
design-build-operate-and-maintain
   (DBOM)   2–3, 4–5
design-build/turnkey   4
design competition   6
design fee: vs construction cost for
   modifications   43 (graph); vs
   construction cost for new
   construction   43 (graph)
detail, lack of: as problem with
   bidding   26
direct costs, other   33
direct labor multiplier   35
direct personal services   11
direct salary times multiplier   35
dispute resolution   50
document ownership   49

EJCDC (Engineers' Joint Contract
   Documents Committee)   47, 50;
   documents   55–60

electronic documents   49
engineering and topographic surveys
   16
Engineering News-Record
   Construction Cost Index History
   45, 45 (table)
engineering services   3–4
engineering services classification
   9–17; construction projects
   11–15; consultation,
   investigations, and studies
   10–11; special services   15–17
Engineers' Joint Contract Documents
   Committee (EJCDC)   47, 50;
   documents   55–60
ENR Construction Cost Index History
   45, 45 (table)
environmental assessment and impact
   statements   17
ethical reputation, as selection factor
   19
existing facilities and structures:
   inspections and evaluations   11
experience, as selection factor   19
expert witness services   7, 16, 31; per
   diem   36, 38

feasibility investigations and reports
   10
fee for services   5
final design phase   12, 13–14
final investigations   16
financial matters, assistance in   10–11
financial resources, as selection factor
   20
fixed price method   31, 32, 39, 48–49
flow chart for selection procedure   28
   (figure)
forms: Architect-Engineer and Related
   Services Questionnaire   20–21,
   24; Architect-Engineer and
   Related Services Questionnaire
   for Specific Projects   22, 24;
   Interview Process Score Sheet
   67; Letter to Consultants Not
   Selected for an Interview   65;
   Letter to Short Listed Consultants
   66; Reference Check Form   64;
   Statement of Qualifications

Evaluation Form   62; Statement of Qualifications Evaluation Summary Form   63

general overhead   33–34
geotechnical engineering   16
graphs: design fee vs construction cost for modifications   43 (graph); design fee vs construction cost for new construction   43 (graph); total fee vs construction cost for modifications   44 (graph); total fee vs construction cost for new construction   44 (graph)

hourly billing rate   36, 37 (table), 48–49

inflation provision   48–49
inspections and evaluations of existing facilities and structures   11
Interview Process Score Sheet   67
interviews   23

judgment, professional   26

land surveys   16
lawsuits   50
Letter to Consultants Not Selected for an Interview   65
Letter to Short Listed Consultants   66
liability insurance, professional   25
licensed professional engineers   19
litigation   50
lobbying   24
lump sum method   31, 32, 39, 48–49

materials engineering and equipment tests   11
minimum service   26
Model Procurement Code for State and Local Governments (American Bar Association)   6
modifications: design fee vs construction cost   43 (graph); total fee vs construction cost   44 (graph)
multiplier method   34–35, 36 (table), 48

National Society of Professional Engineers (NSPE)   47
negotiating phase   12, 14
new construction: design fee vs construction cost   43 (graph); total fee vs construction cost   44 (graph)
"not-to-exceed"amount   25, 30–31
NSPE (National Society of Professional Engineers)   47

open-end contract procedure   25
operation phase   12, 15
other direct costs   33
overhead, general   33–34

partnering   51
payment schedule   32
payroll burden   33
percentage method of charging   29
per diem   36, 38, 48–49
performance evaluation   52
planning studies   10
preliminary and feasibility investigations and reports   10
preliminary design phase   11, 13
preproposal conference   23
prime professional   6, 48
professional judgment   26
professional liability insurance   25
professional responsibility   2
profit   34
program management   4
project cost factors   30–31
project implementation approaches   4–5
public involvement   10

qualifications-based selection (QBS) procedure   21–24; contract   24, 25; evaluation and selection   23–24; as preferred method   25–26; Request for Proposal (RFP)   22–23, 24; requests for qualifications (RFQ)   21–22, 24; short list   22; vs two-envelope system   27
qualifications screening   5
quality   1–2

rate studies   10
redesign   16
Reference Check Form   64
reputation, as selection factor   19
Request for Proposal (RFP)   22–23,
    24
Request for Qualifications (RFQ)
    21–22, 24
responsibility, professional   2
retainage   51
RFP (Request for Proposal)   22–23,
    24
RFQ (Request for Qualifications)
    21–22, 24

salary cost   32
salary cost times multiplier plus direct
    nonsalary expense   34–35, 36
    (table), 48
scope of services   5, 9, 24; assistance
    in financial matters   10–11; and
    charging methods   30–31;
    establishing   27; importance
    29; incomplete   26
selection committee   20
selection procedure flow chart   28
    (figure)
short list: letter to consultants   66;
    qualifications-based selection
    (QBS) procedure   22
special services   15–17, 33; per diem
    36, 38
staff, as selection factor   20, 24
standard of care   50
Statement of Qualifications
    Evaluation Form   62

Statement of Qualifications
    Evaluation Summary Form   63
Statement of Qualifications file
    20–21
study and report phase   11, 12–13
subconsultants   6; contracts with   48
surveys, engineering and topographic
    16

technology, as selection factor   20
termination   51–52
topographic surveys   16
total fee: vs construction cost for
    modifications   44 (graph); vs
    construction cost for new
    construction   44 (graph)
total project cost   41–46; client's costs
    46; construction costs   45–46, 45
    (table); consultant's costs   41–44,
    43 (graph), 44 (graph);
    contingency allowance   46
two-envelope system   27

upset figure   25, 30–31
U.S. government forms: SF   254
    Architect-Engineer and Related
    Services Questionnaire   20–21,
    24; SF   255 Architect-Engineer
    and Related Services
    Questionnaire for Specific
    Projects   22, 24

valuations   10
value engineering   16
value pricing   31
variable reimbursement methods   29,
    30–31